SYMBIOSIS

W9-BEI-353

THE PEARSON CUSTOM LIBRARY FOR THE
BIOLOGICAL SCIENCES

Organismal Biology Lab
BL 126
Loyola University Maryland

Pearson Learning Solutions

New York   Boston   San Francisco
London   Toronto   Sydney   Tokyo   Singapore   Madrid
Mexico City   Munich   Paris   Cape Town   Hong Kong   Montreal

Senior Vice President, Editorial and Marketing: Patrick F. Boles
Senior Sponsoring Editor: Natalie Danner
Development Editor: Annette Fantasia
Assistant Editor: Jill Johnson
Executive Marketing Manager: Nathan L. Wilbur
Operations Manager: Eric M. Kenney
Production Manager: Jennifer Berry
Art Director: Renée Sartell
Cover Designer: Kristen Kiley

Cover Art: Courtesy of Michael R. Martin, Darryl Johnson, Photodisk, DK Images, and Prentice-Hall, Inc.

Pyrex, pHydrion, Chem3D Plus, Apple, Macintosh, Chemdraw, Hypercard, graphTool, Corning, Teflon, Mel-Temp, Rotaflow, Tygon, Spec20, and LambdaII UV/Vis are registered trademarks.

Chem3D Plus is a registered trademark of the Cambridge Soft Corp.

The information, illustrations, and/or software contained in this book, and regarding the above mentioned programs, are provided "as is," without warranty of any kind, express or implied, including without limitation any warranty concerning the accuracy, adequacy, or completeness of such information. Neither the publisher, the authors, nor the copyright holders shall be responsible for any claims attributable to errors, omissions, or other inaccuracies contained in this book. Nor shall they be liable for direct, indirect, special, incidental, or consequential damages arising out of the use of such information or material.

The authors and publisher believe that the lab experiments described in this publication, when conducted in conformity with the safety precautions described herein and according to the school's laboratory safety procedures, are reasonably safe for the students for whom this manual is directed. Nonetheless, many of the described experiments are accompanied by some degree of risk, including human error, the failure or misuse of laboratory or electrical equipment, mismeasurement, spills of chemicals, and exposure to sharp objects, heat, body fluids, blood or other biologics. The authors and publisher disclaim any liability arising from such risks in connections with any of the experiments contained in this manual. If students have questions or problems with materials, procedures, or instructions on any experiment, they should always ask their instructor for help before proceeding.

This special edition published in cooperation with Pearson Learning Solutions.

Printed in the United States of America.

Please visit our web site at *www.pearsoncustom.com.*

Attention bookstores: For permission to return unused stock, contact us at *pe-uscustomreturns@pearson.com.*

Pearson Learning Solutions, 501 Boylston Street, Suite 900, Boston, MA 02116
A Pearson Education Company
www.pearsoned.com

ISBN 10: 0-558-52798-1
ISBN 13: 978-0-558-52798-3

Laboratory Safety: General Guidelines

1. Notify your instructor immediately if you are pregnant, color blind, allergic to any insects or chemicals, taking immunosuppressive drugs, or have any other medical condition (such as diabetes, immunologic defect) that may require special precautionary measures in the laboratory.

2. Upon entering the laboratory, place all books, coats, purses, backpacks, etc. in designated areas, not on the bench tops.

3. Locate and, when appropriate, learn to use exits, fire extinguisher, fire blanket, chemical shower, eyewash, first aid kit, broken glass container, and cleanup materials for spills.

4. In case of fire, evacuate the room and assemble outside the building.

5. Do not eat, drink, smoke, or apply cosmetics in the laboratory.

6. Confine long hair, loose clothing, and dangling jewelry.

7. Wear shoes at all times in the laboratory.

8. Cover any cuts or scrapes with a sterile, waterproof bandage before attending lab.

9. Wear eye protection when working with chemicals.

10. Never pipet by mouth. Use mechanical pipeting devices.

11. Wash skin immediately and thoroughly if contaminated by chemicals or microorganisms.

12. Do not perform unauthorized experiments.

13. Do not use equipment without instruction.

14. Report *all* spills and accidents to your instructor immediately.

15. Never leave heat sources unattended.

16. When using hot plates, note that there is no visible sign that they are hot (such as a red glow). Always assume that hot plates are hot.

17. Use an appropriate apparatus when handling hot glassware.

18. Keep chemicals away from direct heat or sunlight.

19. Keep containers of alcohol, acetone, and other flammable liquids away from flames.

20. Do not allow any liquid to come into contact with electrical cords. Handle electrical connectors with dry hands. Do not attempt to disconnect electrical equipment that crackles, snaps, or smokes.

21. Upon completion of laboratory exercises, place all materials in the disposal areas designated by your instructor.

22. Do not pick up broken glassware with your hands. Use a broom and dustpan and discard the glass in designated glass waste containers; never discard with paper waste.

23. Wear disposable gloves when working with blood, other body fluids, or mucous membranes. Change gloves after possible contamination and wash hands immediately after gloves are removed.

24. The disposal symbol indicates that items that may have come in contact with body fluids should be placed in your lab's designated container. It also refers to liquid wastes that should not be poured down the drain into the sewage system.

25. Leave the laboratory clean and organized for the next student.

26. Wash your hands with liquid or powdered soap prior to leaving the laboratory.

27. The biohazard symbol indicates procedures that may pose health concerns.

The caution symbol points out instruments, substances, and procedures that require special attention to safety. These symbols appear throughout this manual.

Measurement Conversions

Metric to American Standard	American Standard to Metric
Length	
1 mm = 0.039 inches	1 inch = 2.54 cm
1 cm = 0.394 inches	1 foot = 0.305 m
1 m = 3.28 feet	1 yard = 0.914 m
1 m = 1.09 yards	1 mile = 1.61 km
Volume	
1 mL = 0.0338 fluid ounces	1 fluid ounce = 29.6 mL
1 L = 4.23 cups	1 cup = 237 mL
1 L = 2.11 pints	1 pint = 0.474 L
1 L = 1.06 quarts	1 quart = 0.947 L
1 L = 0.264 gallons	1 gallon = 3.79 L
Mass	
1 mg = 0.0000353 ounces	1 ounce = 28.3 g
1 g = 0.0353 ounces	1 pound = 0.454 kg
1 kg = 2.21 pounds	

Temperature

To convert temperature:

$$°C = \frac{5}{9}(F - 32) \qquad °F = \frac{9}{5}C + 32$$

°F / °C thermometer scale:

- 230 / 110
- 220
- 210 / 100 ← Water boils
- 200
- 190 / 90
- 180 / 80
- 170
- 160 / 70
- 150
- 140 / 60
- 130
- 120 / 50
- 110
- 100 / 40
- 98.6°F — Normal human body temperature ← 37.0°C — Normal human body temperature
- 90 / 30
- 80
- 70 / 20
- 60
- 50 / 10
- 40
- 30 / 0 ← Water freezes
- 20 / −10
- 10
- 0 / −20
- −10
- −20 / −30
- −30
- −40 / −40

Centimeters / Inches scale:

- 20 / 8
- 19 / 7
- 18
- 17 / 6
- 16 / 15
- 14 / 5
- 13
- 12 / 4
- 11 / 10
- 9 / 3
- 8
- 7 / 2
- 6 / 5
- 4 / 3
- 2 / 1
- 1 / 0

Contents

Bacteriology
Neil A. Campbell, Jane B. Reece, Judith G. Morgan, M. Eloise Brown Carter 1

Protists and Fungi
Neil A. Campbell, Jane B. Reece, Judith G. Morgan, M. Eloise Brown Carter 35

Plant Diversity: Nonvascular Plants (Bryophytes) and Seedless Vascular Plants
Neil A. Campbell, Jane B. Reece, Judith G. Morgan, M. Eloise Brown Carter 73

Plant Diversity: Seed Plants
Neil A. Campbell, Jane B. Reece, Judith G. Morgan, M. Eloise Brown Carter 99

Animal Diversity: Porifera, Cnidaria, Platyhelminthes, Annelida, and Mollusca
Neil A. Campbell, Jane B. Reece, Judith G. Morgan, M. Eloise Brown Carter 127

Animal Diversity: Nematoda, Arthropoda, Echinodermata, and Chordata
Neil A. Campbell, Jane B. Reece, Judith G. Morgan, M. Eloise Brown Carter 151

Contents

Bacteriology

Laboratory Objectives

After completing this lab topic, you should be able to:

1. Describe bacterial structure: colony morphology, cell shape, growth patterns.
2. Describe the results of Gram staining and discuss the implications to cell wall chemistry.
3. Describe a scenario for succession of bacterial and fungal communities in aging milk, relating this to changes in environmental conditions such as pH and nutrient availability.
4. Practice aseptic techniques producing bacterial streaks, smears, and lawns.
5. Describe the ecology and control of bacteria, applying these concepts to life situations.

Introduction

Humans have named and categorized organisms for hundreds—perhaps even thousands—of years. Taxonomy is an important branch of biology that deals with naming and classifying organisms into distinct groups or categories. Much of the work of early taxonomists included recording characteristics of organisms and grouping them based on appearance, habitat, or perhaps medicinal value. As scientists began to understand the processes of genetics and evolution by natural selection, they realized the value of classifying organisms based on phylogeny, or evolutionary history. Information about phylogeny was obtained from studies of development or homologous features—common features resulting from common genes. In recent years, scientists have begun using biochemical evidence—studies of nucleic acids and proteins—to investigate relationships among organisms, leading to revisions in the taxonomic scheme.

Systematists continue to grapple with the complex challenge of organizing the diversity of life into categories. In the 1960s, Robert Whittaker of Cornell University proposed that scientists use a five-kingdom scheme for classifying living organisms. His scheme was based largely on cell type: prokaryotic or eukaryotic, and nutrition type: autotrophic or heterotrophic. In the 1970s, Carl Woese, a University of Illinois microbiologist, using ribosomal RNA differences proposed a three-domain system that has become widely accepted. The five-kingdom system places all prokaryotic organisms in the kingdom Monera, and eukaryotic organisms are in kingdoms Protista, Fungi, Plantae, and Animalia. In the three-domain system, the three domains—Bacteria, Archaea, and Eukarya—are a taxonomic level higher and include the kingdoms, historically the broadest taxonomic category. In the three-domain system, prokaryotes are placed in one of the two domains Bacteria or Archaea. This classification renders the kingdom Monera obsolete since its members are in two domains. All eukaryotes (organisms that have cells containing true nuclei) are categorized in the domain Eukarya. Three of the kingdoms of the five-kingdom scheme now placed in Eukarya—Fungi, Plantae, and Animalia—are multicellular organisms. Members of the former kingdom Protista are now in the domain Eukarya, but researchers continue to debate the number of kingdoms of protists.

Although many argue that biological categories are subjective in nature and the criteria for designating the kingdoms of life have been modified by scientists historically, it is nonetheless true that scientists have set definite criteria or guidelines that form the basis of taxonomic classification. Most organisms may be placed into these designated categories.

In this lab topic, you will study organisms commonly called **bacteria.** In the three-domain system, the common bacteria are classified in the **domain Bacteria, kingdom Bacteria.**

Bacteria are small, relatively simple, **prokaryotic,** single-celled organisms. **Prokaryotes,** from the Greek for "prenucleus," have existed on Earth longer and are more widely distributed than any other organismal group. They are found in almost every imaginable habitat: air, soil, and water, in extreme temperatures and harsh chemical environments. They can be photosynthetic, using light, or chemosynthetic, using inorganic chemicals as the source of energy, but most are heterotrophic, absorbing nutrients from the surrounding environment.

Most bacteria have a cell wall, a complex layer outside the cell membrane. The most common component found in the cell wall of organisms in the domain Bacteria is peptidoglycan, a complex protein-carbohydrate polymer. There are no membrane-bound organelles in bacteria and the genetic material is not bound by a nuclear envelope. Bacteria do not have chromosomes; their genetic material is a single circular molecule of DNA. In addition, bacteria may have smaller rings of DNA called **plasmids,** consisting of only a few genes. They reproduce by a process called **binary fission,** in which the cell duplicates its components and divides into two cells. These cells usually become independent, but they may remain attached in linear chains or grapelike clusters. In favorable environments, individual bacterial cells rapidly proliferate, forming colonies consisting of millions of cells.

Differences in colony morphology and the shape of individual bacterial cells are important distinguishing characteristics of bacterial species. In Exercise 1, working independently, you will observe and describe the morphology of colonies and individual cells of several bacterial species. You will examine and describe characteristics of bacteria growing in plaque on your teeth. You and your lab partner will compare results of all lab studies.

EXERCISE 1
Investigating Characteristics of Bacteria

Because of the small size and similarity of cell structure in bacteria, techniques used to identify bacteria are different from those used to identify macroscopic organisms. Staining reactions and properties of growth, nutrition, and physiology are usually used to make final identification of species. The structure and arrangement of cells and the morphology of colonies contribute preliminary information that can help us determine the appropriate test necessary to make final identification. In this exercise, you will use the tools at hand, microscopes and unaided visual observations, to learn some characteristics of bacterial cells and colonies.

When you are working with bacteria, it is very important to practice certain **aseptic techniques** to make sure that the cultures being studied are not contaminated by organisms from the environment and that organisms are not released into the environment.

1. Wipe the lab bench with disinfectant before and after the lab activities.

2. Wash your hands before and after performing an experiment.

3. Using the alcohol lamp or Bunsen burner, flame all nonflammable instruments used to manipulate bacteria or fungi before and after use.

4. Place swabs and toothpicks in the disposal container immediately after use. *Never place one of these items on the lab bench after use!*

5. Wear a lab coat, a lab apron, or a clean old shirt over your clothes to lessen chances of staining or contamination accidents.

The bacteria used in these exercises are not pathogenic (disease-producing); nevertheless, use appropriate aseptic techniques and work with care! If a spill occurs, notify the instructor. If no instructor is available, wear disposable gloves, and wipe up the spill with paper towels. Follow this by washing the affected area with soap and water and a disinfectant. Dispose of the gloves and soiled towels in the autoclavable plastic bag provided.

Lab Study A. Colony Morphology

Materials

disinfectant
stereoscopic microscope
metric ruler
agar plate cultures with bacterial colonies

Introduction

A **bacterial colony** grows from a single bacterium and is composed of millions of cells. Each colony has a characteristic size, shape, consistency, texture, and color (colony morphology), all of which may be useful in preliminary species identification. Bacteriologists use specific terms to describe colony characteristics. Use Figure 1 to become familiar with this terminology and describe the bacterial species provided. Occasionally, one or more **fungal colonies** will contaminate the bacterial plates. Fungi may be

Figure 1.
Terminology used in describing bacterial colonies. (a) Common shapes, (b) margins, and (c) surface characteristics are illustrated.

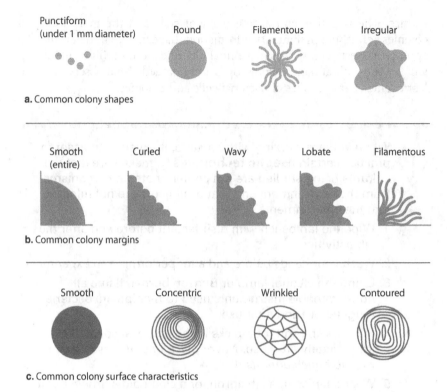

Punctiform (under 1 mm diameter)   Round   Filamentous   Irregular

a. Common colony shapes

Smooth (entire)   Curled   Wavy   Lobate   Filamentous

b. Common colony margins

Smooth   Concentric   Wrinkled   Contoured

c. Common colony surface characteristics

distinguished from bacteria by the *fuzzy* appearance of the colony (Figure 2). The body of a fungus is a mass of filaments called **hyphae** in a network called a **mycelium.** Learn to distinguish fungi from bacteria.

Procedure

1. Wipe the work area with disinfectant and wash your hands.
2. Set up your stereoscopic microscope.
3. Obtain one of the bacterial plates provided. Leaving the plate closed (unless otherwise instructed), place it on the stage of the microscope.
4. Examine a typical individual, separate colony. Measure the size and note the color of the colony, and record this information in Table 1, in the Results section.

Figure 2.
(a) Bacteria and (b) fungi growing on nutrient agar plates. The body of most fungi consists of filaments called *hyphae* in a network called a *mycelium*. The hyphae give fungal colonies a fuzzy appearance.

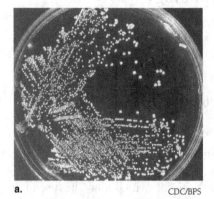

a.   CDC/BPS   b.   CDC/BPS

5. Using the diagrams in Figure 1, select appropriate terms that describe the colony.
6. Record your observations in Table 1.
7. Sketch one colony in the margin of your lab manual, illustrating the characteristics observed.
8. Repeat steps 2 to 6 with two additional species. Your lab partner should examine three different species.

Results

1. Complete Table 1 at the bottom of the page using terms from Figure 1 to describe the three bacterial cultures you observed.
2. Compare your observations with those of your lab partner.

Discussion

1. What are the most common colony shapes, colony margins, and colony surface characteristics found in the species observed by you and your lab partner? The most common colony shapes are round & the most common margins & surface is smooth (as observed by me)

2. Based on your observations, comment on the reliability of colony morphology in the identification of a given bacterial species. Reliable for prelimanary identification

Table 1
Characteristics of Bacterial Colonies

Name of Bacteria	Size	Shape	Margin	Surface	Color
1.	punctiform		smooth	smooth	yellow
2.	round		smooth	smooth	yellow
3.					

Lab Study B. Morphology of Individual Cells

Materials

compound microscope
prepared slides of bacillus, coccus, and spirillum bacteria
blank slide
clean toothpick
clothespin

dropper bottle of deionized (DI) water
dropper bottle of crystal violet stain
squirt bottle of DI water
alcohol lamp or Bunsen burner
staining pan

Introduction

Microscopic examination of bacterial cells reveals that most bacteria can be classified according to three basic shapes: **bacilli** (rods), **cocci** (spheres), and **spirilla** (spirals, or corkscrews). In many species, cells tend to adhere to each other and form aggregates, with each cell maintaining its independence. In this lab study, you will examine prepared slides of bacteria that illustrate the three basic cell shapes, and then you will examine and describe bacteria growing in your mouth.

Procedure

1. To become familiar with the basic shapes of bacterial cells, using the compound microscope, examine prepared slides of the three types of bacteria, and make a sketch of each shape in the space provided.

2. Protein and carbohydrate materials from food particles accumulate at the gum line in your mouth and create an ideal environment for bacteria to grow. This mixture of materials and bacteria is called **plaque.** To investigate the forms of bacteria found on your teeth, prepare a stained slide of plaque.

   a. Set out a clean slide.

   b. Place a drop of water on the slide. This must air-dry, so make the drop of water *small*.

   c. Using a fresh toothpick, scrape your teeth near the gum line and mix the scraping in the drop of water.

   d. Spread this plaque-water mixture into a thin film and allow it to air-dry.

   e. When the smear is dry, hold the slide with a clothespin and pass it quickly over the flame of an alcohol lamp or Bunsen burner several times at a 45° angle. This should warm the slide but not cook the bacteria. Briefly touch the warm slide to the back of your hand. If it is too hot to touch, you are allowing it to get too warm.

6

Keep long hair and loose clothing away from the flame. Extinguish the flame immediately after use.

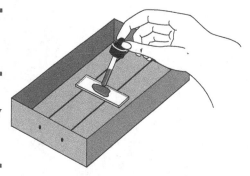

f. Place the slide on the support of a staining pan or tray and apply three or four drops of crystal violet stain to the smear (Figure 3).

Figure 3.
Apply several drops of crystal violet stain to the slide supported in a staining pan or tray.

 Crystal violet will permanently stain your clothes, and it may last several days on your hands as well. Work carefully!

g. Leave the stain on the smear for 1 minute.
h. Wash the stain off with a gentle stream of water from a squirt bottle so that the stain goes into the staining pan (Figure 4).
i. Blot the stained slide gently with a paper towel. Do not rub hard or you will remove the bacteria.

3. Examine the bacteria growing in the plaque on your teeth and determine bacterial forms. Use the highest magnification on your compound microscope. If you have an oil immersion lens, after focusing on the high-dry power, without changing the focus knobs, rotate the high-dry objective to the side, add a drop of immersion oil directly to the bacterial smear, and carefully rotate the oil immersion objective into place. Focus with the fine adjustment only. After observing the slide, rotate the oil immersion objective away from the slide and wipe the objective carefully, using lens paper to remove all traces of oil.

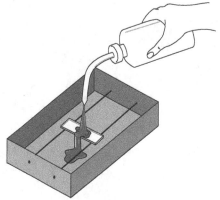

Figure 4.
Gently rinse the stain into the staining pan.

Results

1. Record the individual cell shapes of bacteria present in plaque.

2. What shapes are absent?

3. Estimate the relative abundance of each shape.

Discussion

1. Discuss with your lab partner information you have learned from your dentist or health class about the relationship among plaque, dental caries (cavities), and gum disease.

2. Suggest an explanation for differences in the proportion of each type of bacteria in the bacterial community of plaque.

Lab Study C. Identifying Bacteria by the Gram Stain Procedure

Materials

compound microscope
blank slides
alcohol lamp or Bunsen burner
clean toothpicks
staining pan
cultures of *Micrococcus,*
    Bacillus, Serratia, and *E. coli*

dropper bottles of Gram
    iodine, crystal violet,
    safranin, DI water, 95% ethyl
    alcohol/acetone mixture
squirt bottle of DI water

Introduction

Gram stain is commonly used to assist in bacterial identification. This stain, first developed in 1884, separates bacteria into groups, depending on their reaction to this stain. Bacteria react by testing either **gram-positive, gram-negative,** or **gram-variable,** with the first two groups being the most common. Although the exact mechanisms are not completely understood, scientists know that the response of cells to the stain is due to differences in the complexity and chemistry of the bacterial cell wall. Recall that bacterial cell walls contain a complex polymer, **peptidoglycan.** The cell walls of gram-negative bacteria contain less peptidoglycan than gram-positive bacteria. In addition, cell walls of gram-negative bacteria are more complex, containing various polysaccharides, proteins, and lipids not found in gram-positive bacteria. Gram-staining properties play an important role in bacterial classification.

Gram stain relies on the use of three stains: crystal violet (purple), Gram iodine, and safranin (pink/red). *Gram-positive* bacteria (with the thicker peptidoglycan layer) retain the crystal violet/iodine stain and appear blue/purple. *Gram-negative* bacteria lose the blue/purple stain but retain the safranin and appear pink/red.

In summary:

Gram-Negative Bacteria	Gram-Positive Bacteria
more complex cell wall	simple cell wall
thin peptidoglycan cell wall layer	thick peptidoglycan cell wall layer
outer lipopolysaccharide wall layer	no outer lipopolysaccharide wall layer
retain safranin	retain crystal violet/iodine
appear pink/red	appear blue/purple

In this lab study, you will prepare and stain slides of two different bacterial species. One member of the lab team should stain *Micrococcus* and *Bacillus*. The other member should stain *Serratia* and *E. coli*.

Procedure

1. Using a *clean* slide, prepare smears as directed for the plaque slide (Lab Study B, steps 2a to 2e), substituting the bacterial species for the plaque. If you are using a liquid bacterial culture, do *not* add water to your slide (step 2b). Label the slide with your initials and the name of the bacterial species being investigated.

2. Support the slide on the staining tray and cover the smear with three or four drops of crystal violet. Wait 1 minute.

3. Rinse the stain gently into the staining pan with water from the squirt bottle.

4. Cover the smear with Gram iodine for 1 minute, setting the stain.

5. Rinse it again with water.

6. Destain (remove the stain) by dropping the 95% alcohol/acetone mixture down the slanted slide one drop at a time. At first a lot of violet color will rinse away. Continue adding drops until only a faint violet color is seen in the alcohol rinse. Do not overdo this step (Figure 5). You should be able to see some color in the smear on the slide. If not, you have destained too much. The alcohol/acetone removes the crystal violet stain from the gram-negative bacteria. The gram-positive bacteria will not be destained.

7. Using the water squirt bottle, rinse immediately to prevent further destaining.

Figure 5.
Destain by dropping 95% ethyl alcohol/acetone down the slanted slide until only a faint violet color is seen in the solution.

8. Cover the smear with safranin for 30 to 60 seconds. This will stain the destained gram-negative bacteria a pink/red color. The gram-positive bacteria will be unaffected by the safranin (Figure 6).

9. Briefly rinse the smear with water as above. Blot it lightly with a paper towel and let it dry at room temperature.

10. Examine each slide using the highest magnification on your microscope.

 If you use oil immersion, remove all traces of oil from the objective after observing the slide.

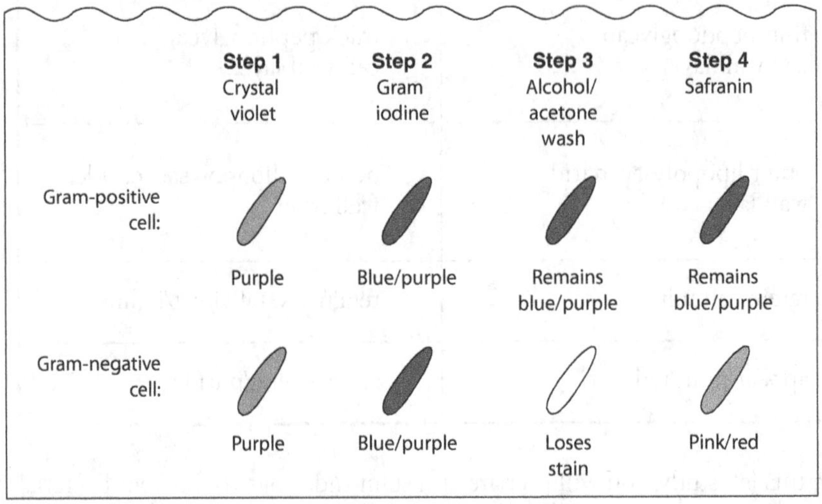

Figure 6.

The Gram stain. Crystal violet and Gram iodine stain all cells blue/purple. Alcohol/acetone destains gram-negative cells. Safranin stains gram-negative cells pink/red.

	Step 1 Crystal violet	Step 2 Gram iodine	Step 3 Alcohol/ acetone wash	Step 4 Safranin
Gram-positive cell:	Purple	Blue/purple	Remains blue/purple	Remains blue/purple
Gram-negative cell:	Purple	Blue/purple	Loses stain	Pink/red

Adapted from E. Alcamo, *Fundamentals of Microbiology*, 5th ed., figure 3.11 (Menlo Park, CA: Benjamin/Cummings, 1997), © 1997 The Benjamin/Cummings Publishing Company.

Results

Record your observations of the results of the Gram stain in Table 2.

Table 2
Bacteria Observed and Results of Gram Stain

Name of Bacteria	Results of Gram Stain
1.	
2.	

Discussion

1. Which of the bacteria observed are probably more closely related taxonomically?

2. What factors can modify the expected results of this staining procedure?

EXERCISE 2
Ecological Succession of Bacteria in Milk

Materials

pH paper
flasks of plain and chocolate whole milk aged 1, 4, and 8 days
TGY agar plates of each of the milk types
supplies from Exercise 1 for Gram stains

Introduction

Milk is a highly nutritious food containing carbohydrates (lactose, or milk sugar), proteins (casein, or curd), and lipids (butterfat). This high level of nutrition makes milk an excellent medium for the growth of bacteria. Pasteurizing milk does not sterilize it (sterilizing kills *all* bacteria) but merely destroys pathogenic bacteria, leaving many bacteria that will multiply very slowly at refrigerated temperatures; but at room temperature, these bacteria will begin to grow and bring about milk spoilage. Biologists have discovered that as milk ages, changing conditions in the milk bring about a predictable, orderly succession of microorganism communities (associations of species).

Community succession is a phenomenon observed in the organizational hierarchy of all living organisms, from bacterial communities in milk to animal and plant communities in a maturing deciduous forest. In each example, as one community grows, it modifies the environment, and a different community develops as a result.

In this laboratory exercise, you will work in pairs and observe successional patterns in two types of milk, plain whole milk and milk with sucrose and chocolate added. You will record changes in the environmental conditions of the two types of milk as they age. Note certain observations scientists have made about milk bacteria and their environment.

1. *Lactobacillus* (gram-positive rod) and *Streptococcus* (gram-positive coccus) survive pasteurization.
2. *Lactobacillus* and *Streptococcus* ferment lactose to lactate and acetic acid.
3. An acidic environment causes casein to solidify, or curd.
4. Two bacteria commonly found in soil and water, *Pseudomonas* and *Achromobacter* (both gram-negative rods), digest butterfats and give milk a putrid smell.
5. Yeasts and molds (both fungi) grow well in acidic environments.

Scenario

Propose a scenario (the hypothesis) for bacterial succession in each type of milk.

On each lab bench are four flasks of plain whole milk and four flasks of chocolate milk. One flask of each has been kept under refrigeration. One flask of each has been at room temperature for 24 hours, one for 4 days, and one for 8 days. On each bench there are also TGY (tryptone, glucose, yeast) agar plate cultures of each of the types of milk.

One team of two students should work with plain milk, another with chocolate milk. Teams will then exchange observations and results.

Procedure

1. Using the pH paper provided, take the pH of each flask. Record your results in Table 3, in the Results section.
2. Record the odor (sour, putrid), color, and consistency (coagulation slight, moderate, chunky) for the milk in each flask.
3. Using the TGY agar plates, observe and describe bacterial/fungal colonies in each age and type of milk. Use the vocabulary you developed while doing Exercise 1.
4. Prepare Gram stains of each different bacterial type on each plate using the staining instructions in Exercise 1, Lab Study C.
5. Record the results of the Gram stains in Table 3, in the Results section.

Results

Complete Table 3, in the Results section, describing the characteristics of each milk culture and the bacteria present in each.

Table 3
Physical Features and Bacterial/Fungal Communities
of Aged Plain and Chocolate Milk

Age/Type Milk	Environmental Characteristics (pH, Consistency, Odor, Color)	Organisms Present (Bacteria: Gram +/-, Shapes; Yeasts or Fungi)
Refrigerated plain		
24-hr plain		
4-day plain		
8-day plain		
Refrigerated chocolate		
24-hr chocolate		
4-day chocolate		
8-day chocolate		

Discussion

1. Describe the changing sequence of organisms and corresponding environmental changes during succession in plain milk. Do the results of your investigation match your hypothesis?

2. Describe the changing sequence of organisms and corresponding environmental changes during succession in chocolate milk. Do the results of your investigation match your hypothesis?

3. Compare succession in plain and chocolate milk. Propose reasons for differences.

4. Propose an experiment to test the environmental factors and/or organisms changing in your proposed scenario for milk succession.

EXERCISE 3

Bacteria in the Environment

Bacteria thrive in a wide variety of natural environments. They are present in all environments where higher forms of life exist, and many flourish in extreme environments where no higher life forms exist—boiling hot springs, extremely salty bodies of water, and waters with extreme pH.

In the following experiments, you will sample different environments, testing for the presence of bacteria and fungi. In Experiment A, pairs of students will investigate one of six different environments. Each pair will report results to the entire class. In Experiment B, your team will investigate an environment of your choice.

Experiment A. Investigating Specific Environments

Materials

sterile agar plates
wax pencil
2 cotton-tipped sterile swabs
bacterial inoculating loop
alcohol lamp or Bunsen burner
piece of raw chicken in a petri dish
soil samples

samples of pond water
plant leaves or other plant parts
hand soap
Parafilm strips
discard receptacle
forceps

Introduction

The instructor will assign team numbers to each pair of students. Each pair (team) of students will sample bacteria and fungi from one of six environments: food supply, soil, air, pond water, a plant structure, and hands. Read the instructions for all investigations. Think about the following questions, and before you begin your investigation, hypothesize about the relative growth of bacteria and fungi in the different environments.

Where in the environment would bacteria be more common, and where would fungi be more common? Would any of these environments be free of bacteria or fungi?

 Seal all plates with Parafilm after preparation! Discard all used swabs in the designated receptacle!

Hypothesis

Hypothesize about the presence of bacteria and fungi in the different environments.

Prediction

Predict the results of the experiment based on your hypothesis (if/then).

Procedure

Team 1

1. Holding the lid in place, invert an agar plate and label the bottom "chicken."

2. Open the dish containing the piece of chicken, and swab the chicken surface using a sterile cotton swab.

 Avoid touching the chicken. Use the swab. Always wash your hands thoroughly after touching raw chicken, owing to the potential presence of *Salmonella*, bacteria that cause diarrhea.

---

3. Isolate bacteria by the **streak plate** method.

   a. Carefully lift the lid of the agar plate to 45° and lightly streak the swab back and forth across the top quarter of the agar (Figure 7a). Close the lid and *discard the swab in the receptacle provided.* Minimize exposing the agar plate to the air.

   b. Flame the bacterial inoculating loop using the alcohol lamp or Bunsen burner. Allow the loop to cool; starting at one end of the swab streak, lightly streak the microorganism in the pattern shown in Figure 7b. Do not gouge the medium.

   c. Reflame the loop and continue to streak as shown in Figure 7c and described in the figure legend.

      By the end of the last streak, the bacteria should be separated and reduced in density so that only isolated bacteria remain. These should grow into isolated, characteristic colonies.

4. Write the initials of your team members, the lab room, and the date on the petri dish.

5. Seal the dish with Parafilm and place it in the area indicated by the instructor.

6. Incubate the culture 1 week and observe results during the next laboratory period.

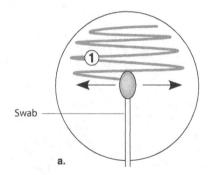
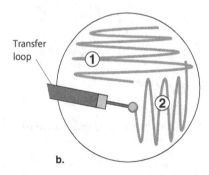
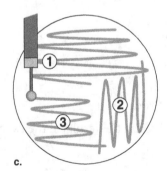

Figure 7.
Isolating bacterial colonies using the streak technique. (a) Streak the swab over the top quarter of the agar plate, region 1. (b) Using the newly flamed loop, pick up organisms from region 1 and streak them into region 2. (c) Reflame the loop and pick up organisms from region 2 and streak them into region 3.

The following week, to avoid exposure to potentially pathogenic bacteria, do not open the petri dish containing the chicken bacteria. Wash hands after handling cultures.

Team 2

1. Holding the lid in place, invert an agar plate and label the bottom "soil."
2. Using a cotton swab, pick up a small amount of soil from the sample.
3. Prepare a streak culture by following step 3 in the procedure for Team 1.
4. Write the initials of your team members, the lab room, and the date on the petri dish.
5. Seal the dish with Parafilm and place it in the area indicated by the instructor.
6. Incubate the culture 1 week and observe results during the next laboratory period.

Team 3

1. Holding the lid in place, invert an agar plate and label the bottom "air."
2. Collect a sample of bacteria by leaving the agar plate exposed (lid removed) to the air in some interesting area of the room for 10 to 15 minutes. Possible areas might be near a heat duct or an animal storage bin.
3. If additional agar plates are available, you may choose to sample several sites.
4. Write the initials of your team members, the lab room, and the date on each petri dish.
5. Seal the dish with Parafilm and place it in the area indicated by the instructor.
6. Incubate the culture(s) 1 week and observe results during the next laboratory period.

Team 4

1. Holding the lid in place, invert an agar plate and label the bottom "pond water."
2. Using a sterile cotton swab, take a sample from the pond water.
3. Prepare a streak culture by following step 3 in the procedure for Team 1.
4. Write the initials of your team members, the lab room, and the date on the petri dish.
5. Seal the dish with Parafilm and place it in the area indicated by the instructor.
6. Incubate the culture 1 week and observe results during the next laboratory period.

Team 5

1. Obtain a sample from a plant. This might be a leaf, a part of a flower, or another plant structure.

2. Holding the lid in place, invert an agar plate and label the bottom "plant _____" naming the part you are testing. If you are testing a leaf, indicate if it is the top or bottom of the leaf.

3. Open the plate and place the plant part flat on the agar surface. You may need to use forceps. Be sure there is good contact. Remove and discard the plant part. Close the petri dish.

4. Write the initials of your team members, the lab room, and the date on the petri dish.

5. Seal the dish with Parafilm and place it in the area indicated by the instructor.

6. Incubate the culture 1 week and observe results during the next laboratory period.

Team 6

1. Draw a line across the center of the bottom of an agar plate. Write "unwashed" on the dish bottom on one side of the line and "washed" on the other side of the line.

2. Select one person who has not recently washed his or her hands to be the test subject. The subject should open the petri dish and *lightly* press three fingers on the agar surface in the half of the dish marked "unwashed." Do not break the agar. Close the petri dish.

3. The subject should wash his or her hands for 1 minute and repeat the procedure, touching the agar with the same three fingers on the side of the dish marked "washed."

4. Write the initials of your team members, the lab room, and the date on the petri dish.

5. Seal the dish with Parafilm and place it in the area indicated by the instructor.

6. Incubate the culture 1 week and observe results during the next laboratory period.

Results

Include results from the entire class.

1. During the following laboratory period, observe your agar cultures of bacteria and fungi from the environment and record your observations in Table 4.

2. Place your agar culture on the demonstration table and make a label of the environment being investigated. All students should observe every culture.

3. Observe the agar plates prepared by your classmates. Record observations in Table 4.

Table 4

Abundance and Types of Colonies Associated with Food
(Raw Chicken), Soil, Air, Water, Plant Structures, and Hands

Environment	Colony Type(s) and Abundance
Chicken	
Soil	
Air	
Pond water	
Plant structure	
Hands before washing	
Hands after washing	

Discussion

1. How did the plates differ in the number and diversity of bacterial and fungal colonies?

2. Did your predictions match your observations? Describe any discrepancies.

3. What factors might be responsible for your results?

4. Based on the results of your experiments, suggest health guidelines for workers in the food industry, as well as for schoolchildren or others who might be concerned with sanitary conditions.

Experiment B. Investigating the Environment of Your Choice

Materials

agar plates   Parafilm strips
sterile swab   discard receptacle
capped test tube of sterile water

Introduction

In the previous experiment, you tested specific environments for the presence of bacteria and fungi. In this lab study, you will study an environment of your choice. If extra agar plates are available, you may choose to investigate bacteria in an environment before and after some treatment, such as bacteria on the water fountain before and after cleaning.

 Seal all plates with Parafilm after preparation!

Hypothesis

Hypothesize about the growth of bacteria in an environment of your choice.

Prediction

Predict the results of the experiment based on your hypothesis.

Procedure

1. Decide what environment you will investigate. It might be some environment in the lab room or somewhere in the biology building. Carry the sterile cotton swab and agar plate to the environment, and use the swab to collect the sample. If you are collecting from a dry surface, you should first dip the cotton swab in the sterile water and then swab the surface. If you apply any treatment to the surface, describe the treatment in the margin of your lab manual.

 Do not do throat or ear swabs! Pathogenic bacteria may be present.

2. Open the agar plate and lightly streak the swab back and forth across the agar. Discard the swab in the receptacle provided.

3. Label the bottom of the agar plate to indicate the environment tested. Record the environment tested in the Results section.

4. Write the initials of your team members, the lab room, and the date on the petri dish.

5. Seal the dish with Parafilm and place it in the area indicated by the instructor.

6. Incubate the culture 1 week and then observe and describe results during the next laboratory period.

Results

1. What environment did you investigate? Indicate any treatment you applied.

2. Characterize the bacterial and fungal colonies from your experiment.

Discussion

1. Do your results match your predictions for the presence of bacteria and fungi in this environment?

2. What factors might be responsible for your results?

EXERCISE 4
Controlling the Growth of Bacteria

Bacteria are found almost everywhere on Earth, and most species are directly or indirectly beneficial to other organisms. Bacteria are necessary to maintain optimum environments in animal and plant bodies and in environmental systems. However, even beneficial species, if they are reproducing at an uncontrolled rate, are potentially harmful or destructive to their environment. In addition, several species of bacteria and fungi are known to be pathogenic, that is, to cause disease in animals and plants. Their growth must be controlled. Agents have been developed that control bacterial and fungal growth. In this exercise, you will investigate the efficacy of three of these growth-controlling agents: antibiotics, antiseptics, and disinfectants.

Lab Study A. Using Antibiotics to Control Bacterial Growth

Materials

agar plate
metric ruler
sterile swab
wax pencil
Parafilm strips

broth cultures of *Micrococcus,*
    Bacillus, Serratia, and *E. coli*
antibiotic dispenser with
    antibiotic disks

Introduction

An **antibiotic** is a chemical produced by a bacterium or fungus that has the potential to control the growth of another bacterium or fungus. Many antibiotics are selective, however, having their inhibiting effect on only certain species of bacteria or fungi. In this lab study, you will apply an assortment of antibiotics to a lawn culture of a bacterial species. Working in pairs, you will determine which antibiotics are able to control the growth of the bacteria. Each pair of students in a group of eight should culture a different bacterium. All four species should be cultured.

A lawn of bacteria is like a lawn of grass—a uniform, even layer of organisms covering an entire surface. Prepare the lawn of bacteria carefully. The success of this experiment will largely depend on the quality of your lawn.

Hypothesis

Hypothesize about the effect of different antibiotics on the growth of bacteria.

Prediction

Predict the results of the experiment based on your hypothesis.

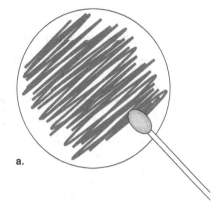

Procedure

1. Label the bottom of an agar plate with your initials, the lab room, the date, and a word to indicate the experiment (such as "antibiotic").

2. Prepare a bacterial lawn.

    a. Insert a sterile swab into the bacterial culture in liquid nutrient broth.

    b. Allow the swab to drip for a moment before taking it out of the culture tube, but do *not* squeeze out the tip. The swab should be soaked but not dripping.

    c. Carefully lift the lid of the agar plate to about 45° and swab the *entire* surface of the agar, taking care to swab the bacteria to the edges of the dish (Figure 8a).

    d. Rotate the plate 45° and swab the agar again at right angles to the first swab (Figure 8b). Close the lid.

3. Carry the agar plate swabbed with bacteria to the demonstration table.

4. Remove the plate lid, place the antibiotic disk dispenser over the plate, and dispense the disks (Figure 9). (Each disk has been saturated with a particular antibiotic. The symbol on the disk indicates the antibiotic name. Your instructor will provide a key to the symbols.)

5. Replace the lid, seal the plate with Parafilm, and place the plate in the area indicated by the instructor. Incubate the dishes at 37°C for 24–48 hours and then refrigerate them.

6. Next week, examine cultures to determine bacterial sensitivity to antibiotics. Measure the diameter of the **zone of inhibition** (area around disk where bacteria growth has been inhibited) for each antibiotic.

7. Record the measurement for your bacterial species and each antibiotic in Table 5. If the antibiotic had no effect on bacterial growth, record the size of the zone as 0.

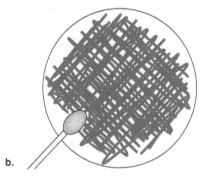

Figure 8.
Preparation of a bacterial lawn.
(a) Apply the bacteria evenly over the entire agar surface. (b) Rotate the plate and swab at right angles to the first application.

Results

1. Using your results and the results from other teams, complete Table 5. Record the sizes of the zone of inhibition for all species of bacteria and all antibiotics.

2. Use the following arbitrary criteria to rank relative bacterial sensitivity to antibiotics:

    NS = not sensitive = no zone of inhibition

    S = sensitive = zone size above 0 but less than 1 cm

    VS = very sensitive = zone size greater than 1 cm

    Write the designation in each blank in the table.

Science VU/BBL/Visuals Unlimited.

Figure 9.
A typical antibiotic dispenser.

Table 5
Results of Antibiotic Sensitivity Tests (Size of inhibition zone for each antibioic is given in centimeters.)

Bacteria (Name, Gram + or −)	Antibiotic						
1.							
2.							
3.							
4.							

Discussion

1. Did your results support your hypothesis? Was the zone of inhibition the same for all bacteria?

2. Were any bacteria very sensitive (greater than 1 cm) to all antibiotics? If so, which bacteria?

3. Based on your results, which antibiotic would you prescribe for each microorganism?

4. Were the results different for gram-positive and gram-negative bacteria?

5. Can you think of alternative explanations for the differential effective-

Lab Study B. Using Antiseptics and Disinfectants to Control Bacterial Growth

Materials

agar plate
forceps
metric ruler
sterile swab
wax pencil
Parafilm strips

broth cultures of *Micrococcus,*
Bacillus, Serratia, and *E. coli*
paper disks soaking in disinfectants
paper disks soaking in antiseptics
paper disks soaking in sterile water

Introduction

Other agents besides antibiotics are often used to control bacterial growth. Those used to control bacteria on living tissues such as skin are called **antiseptics.** Those used on inanimate objects are called **disinfectants.** Antiseptics and disinfectants do not kill all bacteria, as would occur in sterilization, but they reduce the *number* of bacteria on surfaces.

Hypothesis

Hypothesize about the effect of antiseptics and disinfectants on the growth of bacteria.

Prediction

Predict the results of the experiment based on your hypothesis.

Procedure

1. Holding the lid in place, invert a sterile agar plate and label the bottom with your initials, the lab room, and the date. Draw four circles on the bottom. Number the circles.

2. Using the same bacterial culture as you used in Lab Study A, prepare a lawn culture as instructed in Lab Study A.

3. Carry the closed agar plate swabbed with bacteria to the demonstration table.

4. Open the agar plate; using forceps soaking in alcohol, pick up a disk soaked in one of the antiseptics or disinfectants, shake off the excess liquid, and place the disk on the agar above one of the circles. Repeat this procedure with two more antiseptics and/or disinfectants. Place a disk soaked in sterile water above the fourth circle to serve as a control.

5. Record the name of the agent placed above each numbered circle in Table 6. (Example: 1 = Lysol, 2 = Listerine, and so on.) Seal the plate with Parafilm.

6. Place the agar plate in the area indicated by the instructor. Incubate the agar plates at 37°C for 24–48 hours and then refrigerate them.

7. Next week, examine the cultures to determine the bacterial sensitivity to disinfectants and antiseptics. Measure the diameter of the zone of inhibition for each agent.

8. Record the measurement for your bacterial species and each inhibiting agent in Table 6. If the agent had no effect on bacterial growth, record the size of the zone as 0.

Table 6
Results of Sensitivity Tests of Antiseptics and Disinfectants (Size of inhibition zones given in centimeters.)

Bacteria	Antiseptic/Disinfectant/Control			
	1.	2.	3.	4. Control
1.				
2.				
3.				
4.				

Results

1. Using your results and the results from other teams, complete Table 6. Record sizes of the zone of inhibition for all species of bacteria and all antiseptics and disinfectants.

2. Use the following arbitrary criteria to rank relative bacterial sensitivity to antiseptics and disinfectants:

   NS = not sensitive = no zone of inhibition

   S = sensitive = zone size above 0 but less than 1 cm

   VS = very sensitive = zone size greater than 1 cm

   Write the designation in each blank in the table.

Discussion

1. Did your results support your hypothesis? Explain.

2. Based on your results, which disinfectant is most effective in controlling the growth of bacteria?

3. Which antiseptic is most effective?

4. In which situations is it appropriate to use a disinfectant?

An antiseptic?

Questions for Review

1. Once you have completed this lab topic, you should be able to define and use the following terms, providing examples if appropriate: *sterilize, pasteurize, nutrient broth* and *agar, coccus, bacillus, spirillum, antibiotic, antiseptic, disinfectant, peptidoglycan, aseptic technique.*
2. Compare the techniques used to prepare a lawn culture and a streak culture.

Applying Your Knowledge

1. Would you expect the community of bacteria in plaque sampled 1 week *after* you have your teeth cleaned to differ from the community of bacteria found 1 week *before* you have your teeth cleaned? Explain. In your answer, consider the results of the milk succession experiment.

2. Bacterial species that are harmful, as well as others that are beneficial, are found living in the human body. To slow the rate of developing antibiotic resistance in bacteria, physicians are being encouraged to use "narrow spectrum" antibiotics—those that target only a few bacterial types. How can the information learned by antibiotic sensitivity testing be used by physicians who must choose antibiotics that inhibit the growth of bacteria causing disease but that do not interfere with beneficial bacteria?

3. More than 8,000 antiseptics and disinfectants are used to control germs in hospitals, and thousands are available for general use. The efficacy of these agents varies widely, however. Scientists measure the effectiveness of antiseptics and disinfectants in controlling bacterial growth by a standard called the **phenol coefficient** (PC). PC compares a germicidal agent (antiseptic or disinfectant) with phenol, a disinfectant used since the 1860s. A PC of "1" means that the germicide is as effective as phenol in controlling the growth of germs. A substance with a PC greater than "1" is *more* effective than phenol, and a substance with a PC less than "1" is *less* effective than phenol.

Salmonellosis (caused by ingesting *Salmonella* sp.) is one of the most serious foodborne diseases of our time. *Salmonella* bacteria may be found in any food substance but are particularly common on poultry and eggs. Using Table 7 for reference, which germicide would you recommend to control the growth of *Salmonella* in egg- and poultry-processing plants?

Table 7

Phenol Coefficients of Some Common Antiseptics and Disinfectants Used to Control *Staphylococcus* and *Salmonella* Growth*

Germicide	*Staphylococcus*	*Salmonella*
Phenol	1.0	1.0
Iodine	6.3	5.8
Lysol	5.0	3.2
Clorox	133.0	100.0
Ethyl alcohol	6.3	6.3
Hydrogen peroxide	–	0.01
Formalin	0.3	0.7

*Modified from Table 23.2 in Pommerville (2007).

4. Search the Web for information about milk seen in boxes on grocery store shelves. How is this milk prepared? How would you expect bacterial succession in milk prepared in this fashion to differ from succession in milk as investigated in Exercise 2?

5. Death rates due to infectious diseases declined steadily in the United States throughout most of the 20th century. However, since the 1980s, infectious disease-related deaths in the U.S. are increasing significantly. Speculate about possible factors that may be contributing to this increase.

6. In 1929, Alexander Fleming, a Scottish physician, discovered the first antibiotic when he noticed that colonies of certain staphylococcus bacteria growing in culture plates appeared to die when the plates became contaminated with the fungus *Penicillium*. Fleming concluded that a substance diffusing from the fungus into the growth medium was causing the bacteria to lyse (break down), and he called this substance penicillin.

   In its natural environment, what would be the adaptive advantage of a fungus producing and secreting a bacterial inhibitor?

Investigative Extensions

Topics related to bacteriology are popular studies because they apply to many areas of ecology and human health. For example, we are all becoming more aware of the importance of hand washing to prevent the spread of disease, a topic discussed on a popular morning TV show featuring a segment on bacteria in the college environment. In September 2006, the public was notified of contamination of organically grown spinach with *E. coli* 0157:H7, a potentially deadly bacterium. Previously, green onion and fresh lettuce contaminations in popular fast-food restaurants led to a heightened awareness of potential food contamination and changes in agricultural practices. These are just a few of the current issues in bacteriology, and you may design any number of interesting experiments to investigate questions related to bacteriology.

Investigating Soil Bacteria

The study of bacteria is important not only to health professionals, but also to ecologists. Microbial ecologists know the importance of having bacterial diversity in soils in all ecosystems. Certain bacteria in soil serve as decomposers that consume simple carbon compounds releasing inorganic materials useful to other organisms in the soil food web. Other bacteria—for example nitrogen-fixing bacteria, form mutualistic relationships with plants, benefiting both bacteria and plant. Some species of bacteria are important in nitrogen cycling and degradation of pollution, and some soil bacteria are pathogenic and cause plant diseases.

Using ideas and protocols in this laboratory topic, design an experiment to investigate soil microbial diversity. First survey your campus or community and propose possible questions about soil bacteria in your area. For example, you might compare samples of soil taken from the athletic field that is regularly treated with pesticides, from a natural area, a flower garden, a wetland, an organic garden, etc.

Before you begin your experiment, review safety notes and aseptic techniques (Exercise 1). Wear gloves when handling plates and bacteria and wash hands frequently. Remember to keep careful records of procedures and results for each component of your experiment.

After preparing and incubating plates (room temperature is usually adequate) record the numbers of fungal and bacterial colonies on each plate and the morphology—shape and color—of bacterial colonies. Then, using techniques for streaking plates, prepare plates of individual colonies. After the plates have incubated, use laboratory protocols for determining cell shapes and Gram stain characteristics. Look for motility in freshly prepared slides.

With your partners, decide how you will present your results. Design tables and graphs to collect and present data. If digital and/or microscope photographic equipment is available, photograph your plates and the bacteria on your slides. Photographs may be used in a written or oral presentation of your experiment.

Investigating Bacteria and Human Health

Using techniques provided in this lab topic and following aseptic techniques and protocols (Exercise 1), design an experiment to investigate one of the following:

1. Investigate the efficacy of hand washing by varying the type of soap (liquid, bar, antibacterial, deodorant) or the manner of washing (scrubbing time, use of a brush). (Exercise 3)

2. Investigate the efficacy of waterless hand sanitizers in killing bacteria after various activities—for example, using the rest room, touching raw chicken, shaking hands, or cracking a raw egg. Wear disposable gloves when performing this experiment. (Exercise 3)

3. The chicken industry and the FDA have recently been criticized for having low health and safety standards. Pursue this topic by a survey of brands or handling techniques. Health officials now recommend that all eggs be cooked before eating to avoid *Salmonella*. Determine the extent of contamination in store-bought eggs and in eggs from local sources. (Exercise 3)

4. Design an experiment to test bacterial succession in plaque. (Exercise 2)

5. Onions, garlic, green tea, and grapefruit seeds have all been suggested as having antibiotic properties. Design an experiment to test this. (Exercise 4)

Student Media Activities and Investigations

Activities—Ch. 6: Comparing Prokaryotic and Eukaryotic Cells; Ch.26: Classification Schemes; Ch.27: Prokaryotic Cell Structure and Function; Classification of Prokaryotes
www.masteringbio.com

References

Campbell, N., and J. Reece. *Biology*, 8th ed. San Francisco: Benjamin Cummings, 2008.

Dill, B., and H. Merilles. "Microbial Ecology of the Oral Cavity," in *Tested Studies for Laboratory Teaching (Volume 10). Proceedings of the 10th Workshop/Conference of the Association for Biology Laboratory Education (ABLE)*, Corey Goldman, editor, 1989.

Doolittle, W. F. "Uprooting the Tree of Life." *Scientific American* 2000, vol. 282, pp. 90–95.

Gillen, A. L., and R. P. Williams. "Pasteurized Milk as an Ecological System for Bacteria." *The American Biology Teacher* 1988, vol. 50, pp. 279–282.

Hughes, J. M. "Emerging Infectious Diseases: A CDC Perspective." *Emerging Infectious Diseases* 2001, vol. 7, pp. 494–496.

Levy, S. B. "The Challenge of Antibiotic Resistance." *Scientific American* 1998, vol. 278, pp. 46–53.

Nester, E. W., C. E. Roberts, N. N. Pearsall, and B. J. McCarthy. *Microbiology*, 2nd ed. Dubuque, IA: WCB/McGraw-Hill, 1998. Good discussion of ecological succession of microbes.

Pommerville, J. C. *Alcamo's Fundamentals of Microbiology*, 8th ed. Boston: Jones and Bartlett Publishers, 2007. Good discussion of the role of bacteria in dental disease.

Website

Resource for learning about the Domain Bacteria:
http://www.ucmp.berkeley.edu/bacteria/bacteria.html

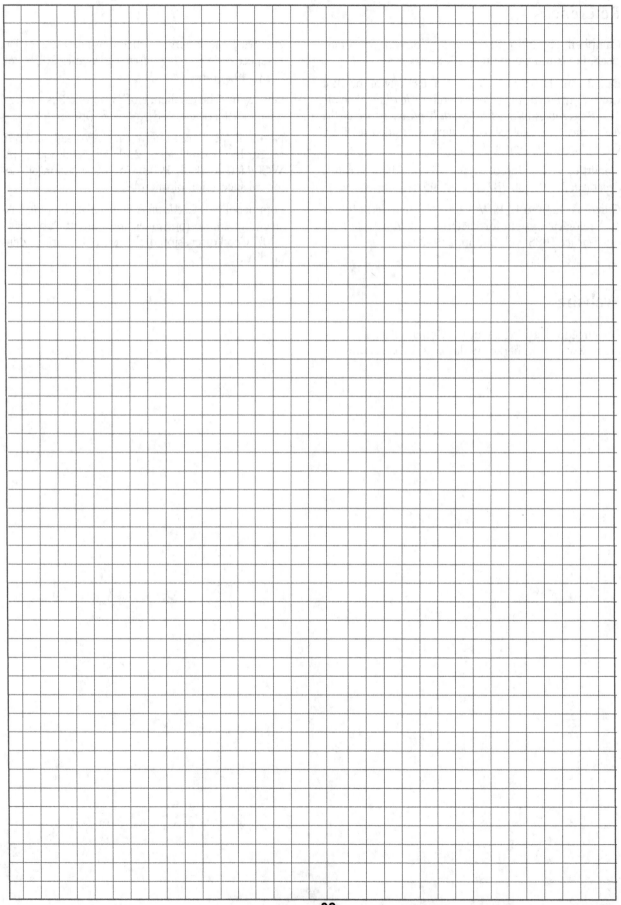

Measurement Conversions

Metric to American Standard	American Standard to Metric
Length	
1 mm = 0.039 inches	1 inch = 2.54 cm
1 cm = 0.394 inches	1 foot = 0.305 m
1 m = 3.28 feet	1 yard = 0.914 m
1 m = 1.09 yards	1 mile = 1.61 km
Volume	
1 mL = 0.0338 fluid ounces	1 fluid ounce = 29.6 mL
1 L = 4.23 cups	1 cup = 237 mL
1 L = 2.11 pints	1 pint = 0.474 L
1 L = 1.06 quarts	1 quart = 0.947 L
1 L = 0.264 gallons	1 gallon = 3.79 L
Mass	
1 mg = 0.0000353 ounces	1 ounce = 28.3 g
1 g = 0.0353 ounces	1 pound = 0.454 kg
1 kg = 2.21 pounds	

Temperature

To convert temperature:

$$°C = \frac{5}{9}(F - 32) \qquad °F = \frac{9}{5}C + 32$$

°F   °C

230 — 110
220
210 — 100 ← Water boils
200
— 90
190
180 — 80
170
160 — 70
150
140 — 60
130
120 — 50
110
— 40
98.6°F — 100 → 37.0°C
Normal human body temperature — 90 — 30 — Normal human body temperature
80
70 — 20
60
50 — 10
40
30 — 0 ← Water freezes
20
10 — −10
0
−20
−10
−20 — −30
−30
−40 — −40

Centimeters   Inches

20 — 8
19 — 7
18
17
16 — 6
15
14
13 — 5
12
11
10 — 4
9
8 — 3
7
6 — 2
5
4
3 — 1
2
1
0 — 0

Laboratory Safety:
General Guidelines

1. Notify your instructor immediately if you are pregnant, color blind, allergic to any insects or chemicals, taking immunosuppressive drugs, or have any other medical condition (such as diabetes, immunologic defect) that may require special precautionary measures in the laboratory.

2. Upon entering the laboratory, place all books, coats, purses, backpacks, etc. in designated areas, not on the bench tops.

3. Locate and, when appropriate, learn to use exits, fire extinguisher, fire blanket, chemical shower, eyewash, first aid kit, broken glass container, and cleanup materials for spills.

4. In case of fire, evacuate the room and assemble outside the building.

5. Do not eat, drink, smoke, or apply cosmetics in the laboratory.

6. Confine long hair, loose clothing, and dangling jewelry.

7. Wear shoes at all times in the laboratory.

8. Cover any cuts or scrapes with a sterile, water-proof bandage before attending lab.

9. Wear eye protection when working with chemicals.

10. Never pipet by mouth. Use mechanical pipeting devices.

11. Wash skin immediately and thoroughly if contaminated by chemicals or microorganisms.

12. Do not perform unauthorized experiments.

13. Do not use equipment without instruction.

14. Report *all* spills and accidents to your instructor immediately.

15. Never leave heat sources unattended.

16. When using hot plates, note that there is no visible sign that they are hot (such as a red glow). Always assume that hot plates are hot.

17. Use an appropriate apparatus when handling hot glassware.

18. Keep chemicals away from direct heat or sunlight.

19. Keep containers of alcohol, acetone, and other flammable liquids away from flames.

20. Do not allow any liquid to come into contact with electrical cords. Handle electrical connectors with dry hands. Do not attempt to disconnect electrical equipment that crackles, snaps, or smokes.

21. Upon completion of laboratory exercises, place all materials in the disposal areas designated by your instructor.

22. Do not pick up broken glassware with your hands. Use a broom and dustpan and discard the glass in designated glass waste containers; never discard with paper waste.

23. Wear disposable gloves when working with blood, other body fluids, or mucous membranes. Change gloves after possible contamination and wash hands immediately after gloves are removed.

24. The disposal symbol indicates that items that may have come in contact with body fluids should be placed in your lab's designated container. It also refers to liquid wastes that should not be poured down the drain into the sewage system.

25. Leave the laboratory clean and organized for the next student.

26. Wash your hands with liquid or powdered soap prior to leaving the laboratory.

27. The biohazard symbol indicates procedures that may pose health concerns.

The caution symbol points out instruments, substances, and procedures that require special attention to safety. These symbols appear throughout this manual.

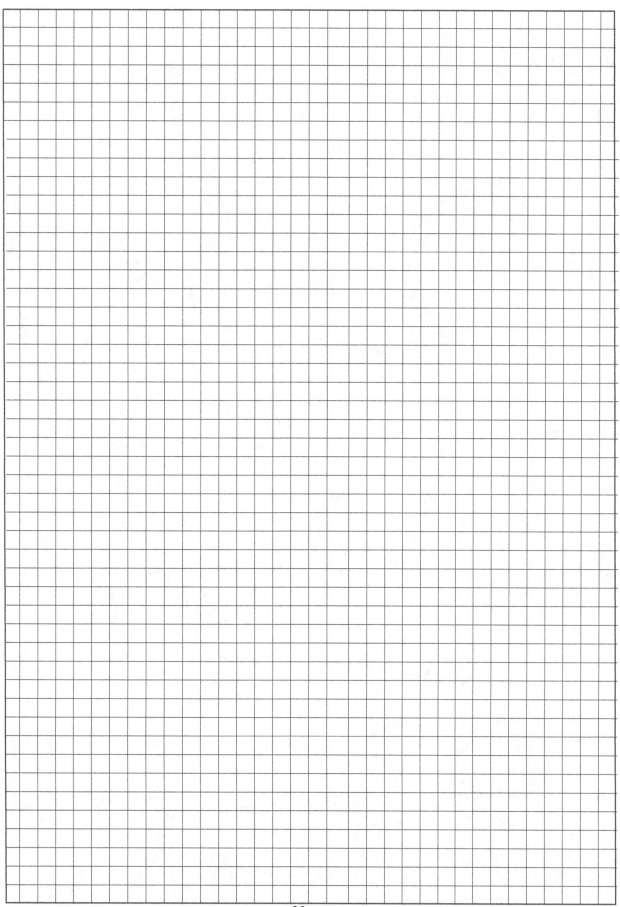

Protists and Fungi

 This lab topic gives you another opportunity to practice the scientific process. Before going to lab, review scientific investigation and carefully read this lab. Be prepared to use this information to design an experiment with protists or fungi.

Laboratory Objectives

After completing this lab topic, you should be able to:

1. Discuss the diversity of protists and fungi, and the current interest in their phylogenetic relationships.
2. Describe the diversity of protists, explaining the means of obtaining nutrition and method of locomotion for each group.
3. Identify representative organisms in several major protistan clades.
4. Discuss the ecological role and economic importance of protists.
5. Describe the characteristics and representative organisms of the green algae and their relationship to land plants.
6. Describe the phyla of the kingdom Fungi, recognizing and identifying representative organisms in each.
7. Describe differences in reproduction in fungal phyla.
8. Discuss the ecological role and economic importance of fungi.
9. Design and perform an independent investigation of a protist or an organism in the kingdom Fungi.

Introduction

Unicellular eukaryotic organisms originated over 2 billion years ago, and today they are found in every habitable region of Earth. The enormous diversity of organisms, their numerous adaptations, and their cellular complexity reflect the long evolutionary history of eukaryotes. For almost 30 years, scientists placed these diverse groups of unicellular organisms into the kingdom Protista. The Protista usually included all organisms not placed in the other eukaryotic kingdoms of Plants, Animals, and Fungi.

From *Investigating Biology Laboratory Manual*, Sixth Edition, Judith G. Morgan and M. Eloise Brown Carter. Copyright © 2008 by Pearson Education, Inc. Published by Benjamin Cummings, Inc. All rights reserved.

This catchall kingdom included not only the unicellular eukaryotes, but also their multicellular relatives, like the giant kelps and seaweeds. However, scientists now agree that the designation kingdom Protista should be abandoned and these eukaryotic organisms that are neither fungi, plants, nor animals, be placed in the domain Eukarya. In this lab topic we will refer to this diverse group as protists meaning a general term, not a taxonomic category.

The most familiar protists, commonly called algae and protozoans, have been well studied since the earliest development of the microscope. Therefore, one might assume that the taxonomic relationships among these groups are well understood. However, their phylogeny (evolutionary history) has been difficult to determine from comparisons of cell structure and function, nutrition, and reproduction. Recent molecular and biochemical research, particularly the ability to sequence ribosomal and transfer RNA genes, has provided strong new evidence for reconstructing the relationships of the protists.

Most recently scientists have suggested that studies of protists using **clades** can be meaningful for indicating evolutionary relationships. A clade is a group of species, all of which are descended from one ancestral species, representing one phylogenetic group. Many characteristics, including molecular and biochemical evidence, are used when organizing clades. As more information from a variety of sources becomes available, major groupings or clades will surely be modified. These investigations into the nature of eukaryotic diversity demonstrate the process of scientific inquiry. New technologies, new ideas, and novel experiments are used to test hypotheses, and the resulting evidence must be consistent with the existing body of knowledge and classification scheme. The results lead to modification of our hypotheses and further research. No matter how many groups or clades are proposed, remember that this is a reflection of the evolution of eukaryotes over the rich history of the earth. It is not surprising that the diversity of life does not easily fit into our constructed categories.

In this lab topic, we will study diverse examples of protists. These protists represent some of the most common clades. In addition to evolutionary relationships, you will give particular attention to nutrition, locomotion, and cellular complexity of each example.

If you complete all of the lab topics in this laboratory manual, you will have studied examples of all the major groups of organisms with the exception of those in domain Archaea. Fungi, one of the kingdoms of the five-kingdom scheme, are studied in this lab topic, and you will investigate plant evolution and animal evolution in subsequent lab topics.

At the end of this lab topic, you will be asked to design a simple experiment to further your investigation of the behavior, ecology, or physiology of one of the organisms studied. As you proceed through the exercises, ask questions about your observations and consider an experiment that you might design to answer one of your questions.

EXERCISE 1
The Protists

In this exercise you will study examples of seven major groups (clades) of protists. (See Table 1 below.)

Table 1
Groups of Protists Investigated in this Exercise

Group	Lab Study	Examples
Euglenozoans	A	*Trypanosoma levisi*
Alveolates	B	Paramecia Dinoflagellates
Stramenopiles	C	Diatoms Brown algae
Foraminiferans and Radiolarians	D	Foraminiferans Radiolarians
Amoebozoans	E	*Amoeba* *Physarum*
Rhodophyta	F	Red algae
Chlorophyta	G	Green algae: *Spirogyra, Ulva, Chara*

Protists may be **autotrophic** (photosynthetic) or **heterotrophic** (depending on other organisms for food). Autotrophic organisms are able to convert the sun's energy to organic compounds. The amount of energy stored by autotrophs is called **primary production**. Traditionally, autotrophic protists are called **algae** and heterotrophic protists are called **protozoa**—protists that ingest their food by **phagocytosis** (the uptake of large particles or whole organisms by the pinching inward of the plasma membrane). Some protozoa, euglenoids for example, are **mixotrophic**, capable of photosynthesis and ingestion. As you investigate the diversity of protists and their evolutionary relationships in this exercise, ask questions about the nutritive mode of each. Note morphological characteristics of examples studied. Ask which characteristics are found in organisms in the same clade and those shared with organisms in other clades or groups. Many of these characteristics are examples of evolutionary convergence. Ask questions about the ecology of the organisms. What means of locomotion do they possess, if any? What role do they play in an ecosystem? Do they have any economic value? Where do they live? (Protists live in a diversity of habitats, but most are aquatic. A great variety of protists may be found in **plankton**, the community of organisms found floating in the ocean or in bodies of freshwater.)

Lab Study A. Euglenozoans—Example: *Trypanosoma levisi*

Materials

compound microscope

prepared slides of *Trypanosoma levisi*

Introduction

Organisms in the clade Euglenozoa are grouped together based on the ultrastructure (structure that can be seen only with an electron microscope) of their **flagella** and their mitochondria. Included in this group are some heterotrophs, some autotrophs, and some parasitic species. The many diverse single-celled and colonial flagellates have been a particular challenge to taxonomists. Under the old two-kingdom system of classification, the heterotrophic flagellates were classified as animals, and the autotrophic flagellates (with chloroplasts) were classified as plants. However, euglenozoans include members of each type. The common flagellated, mixotrophic *Euglena* belongs in this clade.

The organism that you will investigate in this exercise, *Trypanosoma levisi,* moves using flagella supported by microtubules. Organisms in the genus *Trypanosoma* are parasites that alternate between a vertebrate and an invertebrate host. *Trypanosoma levisi* lives in the blood of rats and is transmitted by fleas. Its flagellum originates near the posterior end but passes to the front end as a marginal thread of a long undulating membrane. Another organism in this same genus, *T. gambiense,* causes African sleeping sickness in humans. Its invertebrate host is the tsetse fly.

If you did not observe several other examples of flagellates when you studied the organisms living in a termite's gut, turn to that section of the laboratory manual and, following the procedure, observe these organisms. You may see *Trichonympha* and other flagellates, including *Pyrsonympha* with four to eight flagella, *Trichomonas,* and *Calonympha* with numerous flagella originating from the anterior end of the cell.

Procedure

1. Obtain a prepared slide of *Trypanosoma levisi* (Figure 1) and observe it using low, intermediate, and high powers in the compound microscope.
2. Locate the organisms among the blood cells of the parasite's host.
3. Identify the **flagellum,** the **undulating membrane,** and the **nucleus** in several organisms.

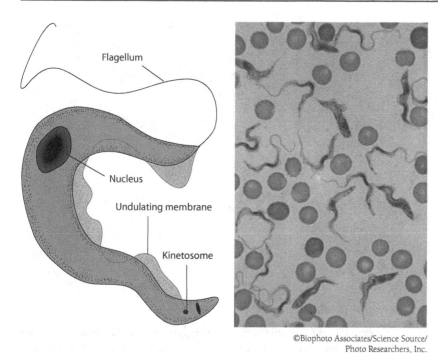

Figure 1.
Trypanosoma, **a euglenozoan,** is a flagellated parasite that lives in the blood of its mammalian host. The flagellum originates near the posterior end, but passes along an undulating membrane to the anterior end.

Results

1. In the margin of your lab manual, draw several representative examples of *T. levisi* and several blood cells to show relative cell sizes.

2. Turn to Table 5 and list the characteristics, ecological roles, and economic importance of *T. levisi.*

Lab Study B. Alveolates—Examples: Paramecia and Dinoflagellates

Materials

compound microscope
slides and coverslips
cultures of living *Paramecium caudata*
Protoslo or other quieting agent
solution of yeast stained with Congo red
cultures of *Paramecium caudata* that have been fed yeast stained with
    Congo red (optional)
dropper bottle of 1% acetic acid
transfer pipettes
living cultures or prepared slides of dinoflagellates

Introduction

Alveolates are single-celled organisms; some are heterotrophic, others autotrophic. The common characteristic of all alveolates is the presence of membrane-bound sac-like structures (**alveoli**) just under the cell membrane. New groupings of protistans into clades place ciliates and dinoflagellates in the Alveolates.

Figure 2.
Paramecium. (a) Complete the drawing of a *Paramecium*, labeling organelles and structures. (b) An enlarged view of cilia and the region of alveoli just under the cell membrane.

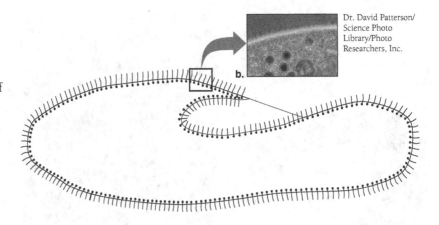

Dr. David Patterson/
Science Photo
Library/Photo
Researchers, Inc.

b.

a.

Paramecium caudatum

The first example you will investigate in this lab study is *Paramecium caudatum*, a heterotrophic organism that moves about using cilia (short projections from the cell surface). Cilia are generally shorter and more numerous than flagella. Internally both structures are similar in their microtubular arrangement.

Procedure

1. Using the compound microscope, examine a living *Paramecium* (Figure 2). Place a drop of water from the bottom of the culture on a clean microscope slide. Add a *small* drop of Protoslo or some other quieting solution to the water drop, then add the coverslip.

2. Observe paramecia on the compound microscope using low, then intermediate powers.

3. Describe the movement of a single paramecium. Does movement appear to be directional or is it random? Does the organism reverse direction only when it encounters an object, or does it appear to reverse direction even with no obstruction?

4. Locate a large, slowly moving organism, switch to high power and identify the following organelles:

   Oral groove: depression in the side of the cell that runs obliquely back to the mouth that opens into a **gullet.**

   Food vacuole: forms at the end of the gullet. Food vacuoles may appear as dark vesicles throughout the cell.

   Macronucleus: large, grayish body in the center of the cell. The macronucleus has many copies of the genome and controls most cellular activities, including asexual reproduction.

   Micronucleus: often difficult to see in living organisms, this small round body may be lying close to the macronucleus. Micronuclei are involved in sexual reproduction. Many species of paramecia have more than one micronucleus.

   Contractile vacuole: used for water balance, two of these form, one at each end of the cell. Each contractile vacuole is made up of a ring of radiating tubules and a central spherical vacuole. Your organism may be under osmotic stress because of the Protoslo, and the contractile vacuoles may be filling and collapsing as they expel water from the cell.

5. Observe feeding in a paramecium. Add a drop of yeast stained with Congo red to the edge of the coverslip and watch as it diffuses around the paramecium. Study the movement of food particles from the oral groove to the gullet to the formation of a food vacuole that will subsequently move through the cell as the food is digested in the vacuole. You may be able to observe the discharge of undigested food from the food vacuole at a specific site on the cell surface.

6. Observe the discharge of **trichocysts,** structures that lie just under the outer surface of the paramecium. When irritated by a chemical or attacked by a predator, the paramecium discharges these long thin threads that may serve as a defense mechanism, as an anchoring device, or to capture prey. Make a new slide of paramecia. Add a drop of 1% acetic acid to the edge of the coverslip and carefully watch a paramecium. Describe the appearance of trichocysts in this species.

Results

1. Complete the drawing of a paramecium (Figure 2), labeling all the organelles and structures shown in bold in the text.

2. Turn to Table 5 and list the characteristics, ecological roles, and economic importance of paramecia.

 Student Media Videos—Ch. 28: Paramecium Vacuole; Paramecium Cilia

Dinoflagellates

Swirl your hand through tropical ocean waters at night and you may notice a burst of tiny lights. Visit a warm, stagnant inlet and you might notice that the water appears reddish and dead fish are floating on the surface. Both of these phenomena may be due to activities of dinoflagellates—single-celled organisms that are generally photosynthetic. Some dinoflagellates are able to bioluminesce, or produce light. They sometimes can *bloom* (reproduce very rapidly) and cause the water to appear red from pigments in their bodies. If the organisms in this "red tide" are a species of dinoflagellate that releases toxins, fish and other marine animals can be poisoned. Red tides in the Chesapeake Bay are thought to be caused by *Pfiesteria,* a dinoflagellate that produces deadly toxins resulting in invertebrate and fish kills, and that also may be implicated in human illness and death. Dinoflagellates have a cellulose cell wall often in the form of an armor of numerous plates with two perpendicular grooves, each containing a flagellum. Most of these organisms are autotrophic and play an important role in **primary production** in oceans—photosynthesis that ultimately provides food for all marine organisms.

Dinoflagellates have traditionally been considered algae, but they are now thought to share a common ancestor with ciliates, as evidenced by the presence of alveoli.

Procedure

1. Obtain a prepared slide or make a wet mount of dinoflagellates (Figure 3).

2. Focus the slide on low power and attempt to locate the cells. You may have to switch to intermediate power to see them.

Figure 3.
Dinoflagellates.
The cell wall is made of cellulose plates with two perpendicular grooves, each containing a flagellum.

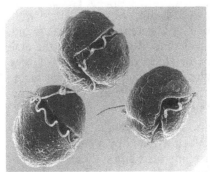
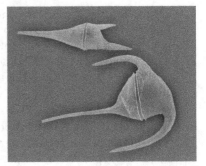

Dr. David M. Phillips/Visuals Unlimited

Dr. Dennis Kunkel/Visuals Unlimited

3. Switch to high power.
4. Identify the perpendicular **grooves** and the **cellulose plates** making up the cell wall. Are the plates in your species elongated into spines? **Flagella** may be visible in living specimens.

Results

1. Draw several examples of cell shapes in the margin of your lab manual. Note differences between the species on your slide and those in Figure 3.
2. Turn to Table 5 and list the characteristics, ecological roles, and economic importance of dinoflagellates.

 Student Media Video—Ch. 28: Dinoflagellate

Lab Study C. Stramenopiles— Examples: Diatoms and Brown Algae

Materials

compound microscope
slides and coverslips
living cultures of diatoms
transfer pipettes
prepared slides of diatomaceous earth (demonstration only)
demonstration materials of brown algae

Introduction

The clade Stramenopila includes water molds (phylum Oomycetes), diatoms (phylum Bacillariophyta), golden algae (phylum Chrysophyta), and brown algae (phylum Phaeophyta). These organisms are grouped in this clade based on the structure of their flagella (when present). The flagellum has many hair-like lateral projections.

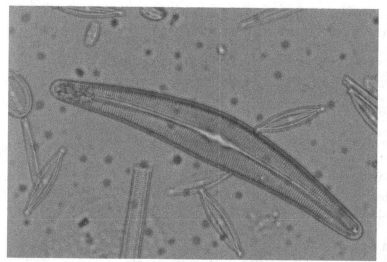 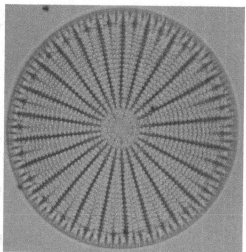

Figure 4.   Sidney Moulds/Photo Researchers, Inc.   John Burbidge/Photo Researchers, Inc.

Diatoms are important autotrophs found in plankton. Many different species and forms exist. All have cell walls made of silica.

In this lab study you will investigate two examples: diatoms and brown algae. Both are autotrophic organisms that play an important role in primary production in oceans.

Diatoms (Bacillariophyta)

Diatoms are important autotrophic organisms in plankton. In fact, they are the most important photosynthesizers in cold marine waters. They can be unicellular, or they can aggregate into chains or star-like groups. Protoplasts of these organisms are enclosed by a cell wall made of silica that persists after the death of the cell. These cell wall deposits are mined as **diatomaceous earth** and have numerous economic uses (for example, in swimming pool filters and as an abrasive in toothpaste and silver polish). Perhaps the greatest value of diatoms, however, is the carbohydrate and oxygen they produce that can be utilized by other organisms. Ecologists are concerned about the effects of acid rain and changing climatic conditions on populations of diatoms and their rate of primary productivity.

Diatom cells are either elongated, boat-shaped, bilaterally symmetrical **pennate** forms or radially symmetrical **centric** forms. The cell wall consists of two valves, one fitting inside the other, in the manner of the lid and bottom of a petri dish.

Procedure

1. Prepare a wet mount of diatoms (Figure 4) from marine plankton samples or other living cultures.
2. Observe the organisms on low, intermediate, and high powers.
3. Describe the form of the diatoms in your sample. Are they centric, pennate, or both?

4. If you are studying living cells, you may be able to detect locomotion. The method of movement is uncertain, but it is thought that contractile fibers just inside the cell membrane produce waves of motion on the cytoplasmic surface that extends through a groove in the cell wall. What is the body form of motile diatoms?

5. Observe a single centric form on high power and note the intricate geometric pattern of the cell wall. Can you detect the two valves?

6. Look for chloroplasts in living forms.

7. Observe diatomaceous earth on demonstration and identify pennate and centric forms.

Results

1. Sketch several different shapes of diatoms in the margin of your lab manual.

2. Turn to Table 5 and list the characteristics, ecological roles, and economic importance of diatoms.

Student Media Videos—Ch. 28: Diatoms Moving; Various Diatoms

Brown Algae (Phaeophyta)

Some of the largest algae, the **kelps**, are brown algae. The Sargasso Sea is named after the large, free-floating brown algae *Sargassum*. These algae appear brown because of the presence of the brown pigment **fucoxanthin** in addition to chlorophyll *a*. Brown algae are perhaps best known for their commercial value. Have you ever wondered why commercial ice cream is smoother in texture than homemade ice cream? Extracts of **algin**, a polysaccharide in the cell wall of some brown algae, are used commercially as thickening or emulsifying agents in paint, toothpaste, ice cream, pudding, and in many other commercial food products. *Laminaria*, known as *kombu* in Japan, is added to soups, used to brew a beverage, and covered with icing as a dessert.

Procedure

Observe examples of brown algae on demonstration (Figure 5).

Results

1. In Table 2, list the names and distinguishing characteristics of each brown algal species on demonstration. Compare the examples with those illustrated in Figure 5.

2. Turn to Table 5 and list the key characteristics, ecological roles, and economic importance of brown algae.

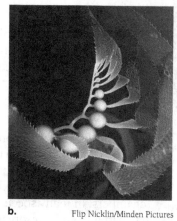

a.

b. Flip Nicklin/Minden Pictures

c. Mark Spencer/Auscape/Minden Pictures

Figure 5.

Examples of multicellular brown algae (phylum Phaeophyta). The body of a brown alga consists of broad blades, a stemlike stipe, and a holdfast for attachment. These body parts are found in the kelps (a) Sea palm (*Postelsia*) and (b) *Nereocystis*. Rounded air bladders for flotation are seen in (c) *Sargassum* and other species of brown algae.

Table 2

Representative Brown Algae

Name	Body Form (single-celled, filamentous, colonial, leaf-like; broad or linear blades)	Characteristics (pigments, reproductive structures, structures for attachment and flotation)

Lab Study D. Foraminiferans and Radiolarians

Materials

compound microscope
prepared slides of foraminiferans
prepared slides of radiolarian skeletons (demonstration only)

Figure 6.
Forams are heterotrophic organisms that move using thread-like pseudopodia. Their shell-like tests are made of calcium carbonate.

Manfred Kage/Peter Arnold, Inc.

Introduction

Foraminiferans and radiolarians are closely related groups composed of ameboid, heterotrophic organisms with **thread-like pseudopodia** or cellular extensions used in feeding and, in some species, locomotion. You will study examples of foraminiferans and radiolarians.

Foraminiferans

Foraminiferans, commonly called **forams,** are another example of organisms that move and feed using pseudopodia. Forams are marine planktonic (freely floating) or benthic (bottom dwelling) organisms that secrete a calcium carbonate shell-like *test* (a hard outer covering) made up of chambers. In many species, the test consists of chambers secreted in a spiral pattern, and the organism resembles a microscopic snail. Although most forams are microscopic, some species, called *living sands,* may grow to the size of several centimeters, an astounding size for a single-celled protist. Thread-like pseudopodia extend through special pores in the calcium carbonate test. The test can persist after the organism dies, becoming part of marine sand. Remains of tests can form vast limestone deposits.

Procedure

1. Obtain a prepared slide of representative forams (Figure 6).
2. Observe the organisms first on the lowest power of the compound microscope and then on intermediate and high powers.
3. Note the arrangement and attempt to count the number of chambers in the test. In most species, the number of chambers indicates the relative age of the organisms, with older organisms having more chambers. Which are more abundant on your slide, older or younger organisms?

   Chambers can be arranged in a single row, in multiple rows, or wound into a spiral. Protozoologists determine the foram species based on the appearance of the test. Are different species present?

Results

1. Sketch several different forams in the margin of your lab manual. Note differences in the organisms on your slide and those depicted in Figure 6.
2. Turn to Table 5 and list the characteristics, ecological roles, and economic importance of forams.

Radiolarians

The **radiolarians** studied here are common in marine plankton. They secrete skeletons of silicon dioxide that can, as with the forams, collect in vast deposits on the ocean floor. Their thread-like pseudopodia, called **axopodia,** extend outward through pores in the skeleton in all directions from the central spherical cell body.

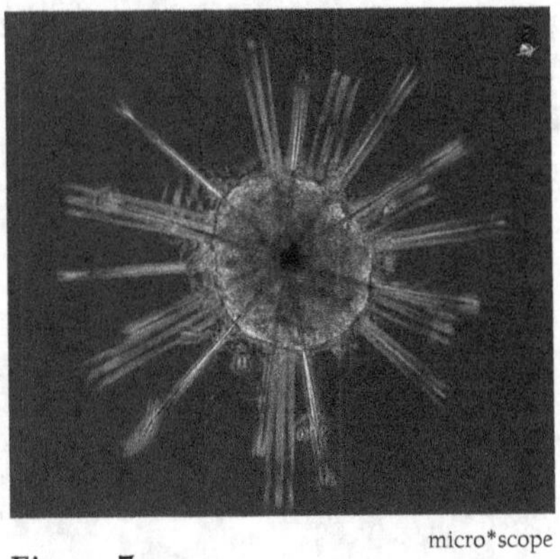

micro*scope

Figure 7.
Radiolarians are supported by a skeleton of silicon dioxide. They use thread-like pseudopodia to obtain food.

Procedure

1. Observe slides of radiolarians on demonstration (Figure 7).
2. Observe the size and shape of the skeletons and compare your observations with Figure 7.

Results

1. Sketch several different radiolarians skeletons in the margin of your lab manual, noting any differences between the organisms on demonstration and those in the figure.

2. Turn to Table 5 and list the characteristics, ecological roles, and economic importance of radiolarians.

Lab Study E. Amoebozoans—Examples: *Amoeba,* Slime Molds

Materials

cultures of *Amoeba proteus*
slides and coverslips (for amoeba)
stereoscopic microscopes
Physarum growing on agar plates

Introduction

Amebozoans have pseudopodia as seen in foraminiferia and radiolarians, but the structure is different. Rather than thread-like pseudopodia as seen in these organisms, amebozoans' pseudopodia are *lobe-shaped*. Based on their ameboid characteristics, their phagocytic mode of obtaining nutrition, and molecular systematics, both amoeba and slime molds are included in the clade **Amoebozoa.**

Amoeba

You have studied **Amoeba proteus,** a protozoan species of organisms that move using lobed-shaped pseudopodia. Amoeba have no fixed body shape and they are naked; that is, they do not have a shell. Different species may be found in a variety of habitats, including freshwater and marine habitats. Recall that pseudopodia are cellular extensions. As the pseudopod extends, endoplasm flows into the extension. By extending several pseudopodia in sequence and flowing into first one and then the next, the amoeba proceeds along in an irregular, slow fashion. Pseudopodia are also used to capture and ingest food. When a suitable food particle such as a bacterium, another protist, or a piece of detritus (fragmented remains of dead organisms) contacts an amoeba, a pseudopod will flow completely around the particle and take it into the cell by phagocytosis.

If you did not observe *Amoeba proteus* or some other naked amoeba, turn to that section of the laboratory manual and, following the procedure, observe these organisms.

 Student Media Videos—Ch. 28: Amoeba; Amoeba Pseudopodia

Slime Molds (Mycetozoa)

William Crowder, in a classic *National Geographic* article (April 1926) describes his search for strange creatures in a swamp on the north shore of Long Island. This is his description of his findings: "Behold! Seldom ever before had such a gorgeous sight startled my unexpectant gaze. Spreading out over the bark [of a dead tree] was a rich red coverlet . . . consisting of thousands of small, closely crowded, funguslike growths. . . . A colony of these tiny organisms extended in an irregular patch . . . covering an area nearly a yard in length and slightly less in breadth. . . . Each unit, although actually less than a quarter of an inch in height, resembled . . . a small mushroom, though more marvelous than any I have ever seen."

The creatures described by Crowder are heterotrophic organisms called **slime molds.** They have been called plants, fungi, animals, fungus animals, protozoa, Protoctista, Protista, Mycetozoa, and probably many more names. Classifying slime molds as fungi (as in previous classification schemes) causes difficulties because whereas slime molds are phagocytic like protozoa, fungi are never phagocytic but obtain their nutrition by absorption. Characteristics other than feeding mode, including cellular ultrastructure, cell wall chemistry, and other molecular studies, indicate that slime molds fit better with the ameboid protists than with the fungi. These studies suggest that slime molds descended from unicellular amoeba-like organisms.

There are two types of slime molds, plasmodial slime molds and cellular slime molds. In this lab study, you will observe the plasmodial slime mold *Physarum.* The vegetative stage is called a **plasmodium,** and it consists of a multinucleate mass of protoplasm totally devoid of cell walls. This mass feeds on bacteria as it creeps along the surface of moist logs or dead leaves. When conditions are right, it is converted into one or more reproductive structures, called **fruiting bodies,** that produce spores. You may choose to investigate slime molds further in Exercise 3.

Procedure

1. Obtain a petri dish containing *Physarum* and return to your lab bench to study the organism. Keep the dish closed.

2. With the aid of your stereoscopic microscope, examine the plasmodium (Figure 8). Describe characteristics such as color, size, and shape. Look for a system of branching veins. Do you see any movement? Speculate about the source of the movement. Is the movement unidirectional or bidirectional—that is, flows first in one direction and then in the other? Your instructor may have placed oat flakes or another food source on the agar. How does the appearance of the plasmodium change as it contacts a food source?

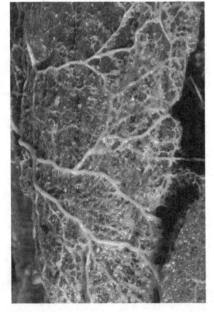

Figure 8.
Slime mold. Slime molds are protists that share some characteristics with both protozoa and fungi. The vegetative stage of a plasmodial slime mold includes an amoeboid phase consisting of a multinucleate mass known as a plasmodium.

3. Examine the entire culture for evidence of forming or mature fruiting bodies. Are the fruiting bodies stalked or are they sessile, that is, without a stalk? If a stalk is present, describe it.

Results

1. Sketch the plasmodium and fruiting bodies in the margin of your lab manual. Label structures where appropriate.

2. Turn to Table 5 and list the characteristics, ecological roles, and economic importance of slime molds.

 Student Media Videos—Ch. 28: Plasmodial Slime Mold Streaming; Plasmodial Slime Mold

---

Lab Study F: Red Algae (Rhodophyta)

Materials

examples of red algae on demonstration

Introduction

The simplest red algae are single celled, but most species have a macroscopic, multicellular body form. The red algae, unlike all the other algae, do not have flagella at any stage in their life cycle. Some scientists suggest that the red algae represent a monophyletic (having a single origin) group and should be placed in their own kingdom. Red algae are autotrophic, containing chlorophyll *a* and the accessory pigments **phycocyanin** and **phycoerythrin** that often mask the chlorophyll, making the algae appear red. These pigments absorb green and blue wavelengths of light that penetrate deep into ocean waters. Many red algae also appear green or black or even blue, depending on the depth at which they are growing. Because of this, color is not always a good characteristic to use when determining the classification of algae. You may have already grown bacteria and fungi on plates of agar. This substance, **agar,** is a polysaccharide extracted from the cell wall of red algae. Another extract of red algae cell walls, **carrageenan,** is used to give the texture of thickness and richness to foods such as dairy drinks and soups. In Asia and elsewhere, the red algae *Porphyra* (known as *nori*) are used as seaweed wrappers for sushi. The cultivation and production of *Porphyra* constitute a billion-dollar industry.

Procedure

Observe the examples of red algae that are on demonstration (Figure 9).

Results

1. In Table 3, list the names and distinguishing characteristics of the red algae on demonstration. Compare the demonstration examples with those illustrated in Figure 9.

2. Turn to Table 5 and list the key characteristics, ecological roles, and economic importance of red algae.

a. b. c.

Figure 9.
Examples of multicellular red algae (phylum Rhodophyta). (a) Some red algae have deposits of carbonates of calcium and magnesium in their cell walls and are important components of coral reefs. (b) Most red algae have delicate, finely dissected blades. (c) *Porphyra* (or *nori*) is used to make sushi.

Table 3
Representative Red Algae

Name	Body Form (single-celled, filamentous, colonial, leaf-like)	Characteristics (reproductive structures, structures for attachment or flotation, pigments)

Lab Study G. Green Algae (Chlorophyta)— The Protist-Plant Connection

Materials

cultures or prepared slides of *Spirogyra* sp.
preserved *Ulva lactuca*
preserved *Chara* sp.

Introduction

The green algae include unicellular motile and nonmotile, colonial, filamentous, and multicellular species that inhabit primarily freshwater environments. Because green algae share many characteristics with land plants, including storage of amylose (starch) and the presence of chlorophylls *a* and *b*, photosynthetic pathways, and organic compounds called flavonoids, most botanists support the hypothesis that plants evolved from green algae. Results of recent work in sequencing ribosomal and transfer RNA genes confirm the close relationship between green algae and land plants, and have led some scientists to propose that green algae, or at least those known as charophytes, be included in the Plant kingdom. In this exercise you will view several body forms of green algae on demonstration: single-celled, filamentous, colonial, and multicellular. Finally, you will observe the multicellular, branched green algae *Chara* (the stonewort), believed to be most similar to the green algae that gave rise to land plants over 475 million years ago.

If you completed a lab titled Microscopes and Cells, you may remember observing aggregates of single-celled algae, *Protococcus*, and the colonial green algae *Volvox*. In this lab study you will observe the filamentous alga *Spirogyra* and the multicellular algae *Ulva* and *Chara*.

Procedure

1. Using your compound microscope, observe living materials or prepared slides of the filamentous alga *Spirogyra* (Figure 10a). This organism is common in small, freshwater ponds. The most obvious structure in the cells of the filament is a long chloroplast. Can you determine how the alga got its name? Describe the appearance of the chloroplast.

   Can you see a nucleus in each cell of the filament?

2. Observe the preserved specimen of *Ulva* sp., commonly called sea lettuce (Figure 10b). This multicellular alga is commonly found on rocks or docks in marine and brackish water.

   a. Describe the appearance and body form of *Ulva*.

   b. Are structures present that would serve to attach *Ulva* to its substrate (dock or rock)? If so, describe them.

   c. Compare your specimen of *Ulva* with that shown in the figure.

3. Examine the preserved specimen of the multicellular green alga *Chara* (Figure 10c). This alga grows in muddy or sandy bottoms of clear lakes or ponds. Its body form is so complex that it is often mistaken for a plant, but careful study of its structure and reproduction confirms its classification as a green alga.

   Note the cylindrical branches attached to nodes. Compare your specimen to Figure 10c. Sketch the appearance of your specimen in the margin of your lab manual.

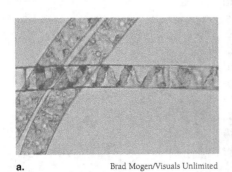

a. Brad Mogen/Visuals Unlimited b. Manfred Kage/Peter Arnold, Inc. c.

Figure 10.
Examples of multicellular green algae (phylum Chlorophyta). (a) A filamentous green alga, *Spirogyra*. (b) Some green algae are multicellular as in *Ulva*, sea lettuce. (c) A multicellular, branched green alga, *Chara*.

Results

1. In Table 4, list the names and distinguishing characteristics of each green algal species studied. Compare these examples with those illustrated in Figure 10.

2. Turn to Table 5 and list the key characteristics, ecological roles, and economic importance of green algae.

Table 4
Representative Green Algae

Name	Body Form (single-celled, filamentous, colonial, leaf-like)	Characteristics (pigments, specialized structures, flagella, structures for attachment)
Spirogyra		
Ulva		
Chara		

Discussion

1. Describe the mechanism for feeding in amoeboid, flagellated, and ciliated protozoans.

2. How do you think amoeboid organisms with skeletons, such as the radiolarians, move food to their cell bodies?

3. Compare the appearance and rate of locomotion in amoeboid, flagellated, and ciliated organisms observed in this exercise.

4. Describe mechanisms for defense in the organisms studied.

5. Compare dinoflagellates and diatoms. What important ecological role is shared by these two groups?

6. What is one characteristic that you could observe under the microscope to distinguish diatoms and dinoflagellates?

7. Slime molds were once placed in the kingdom Fungi. What characteristics suggest that these organisms are protistan?

8. What important ecological role is shared by the macroscopic algae (green, red, and brown)?

9. Based on your observations in the laboratory, what two characteristics might you use to distinguish brown and red algae?

EXERCISE 2

The Kingdom Fungi

Introduction

The kingdom Fungi includes a diverse group of organisms that play important economic and ecological roles. These organisms are unicellular (yeasts) or multicellular, heterotrophic organisms that obtain their nutrients by absorption, digesting their food outside their bodies and absorbing the digestion products into their cells. They often have complex life cycles with alternating sexual and asexual (vegetative) reproduction. They may produce spores either asexually by mitosis or sexually by meiosis.

Fungi are beneficial to humans in many ways. The fungus *Penicillium* is used to produce antibiotics. Yeast, a single-celled fungus, is used in the production of wine, beer, and leavened bread. Fungi are also a source of food in many cultures, with truffles being the most expensive. Black truffles are dark, edible subterranean fungi that sell for $350–$500 per pound. In the United States they grow under specific species of trees in forests in Washington and Oregon. They are located by specially trained truffle-sniffling pigs or dogs. Truffles cannot be grown in a lab or greenhouse.

In ecosystems, fungi share with bacteria the essential role of decomposition, returning to the ecosystem the matter trapped in dead organisms. One extremely important ecological role played by fungi is their mutualistic association with roots of most plants, forming "mycorrhizae." Mycorrhizal fungi increase the plant's ability to capture water and provide the plant with minerals and essential elements. This association greatly enhances plant growth, and may have played a role in plant colonization of land.

Although many fungi are beneficial, others play destructive roles in nature. Some species parasitize animals and plants. Athlete's foot and ringworm are diseases commonly known to humans. Histoplasmosis is a respiratory disease in humans caused by a fungus found in soil and in bat and bird droppings. Wheat rust, potato late blight, and sudden oak death (a potentially devastating disease discovered in the United States in 1995) are plant diseases caused by fungi. The ergot fungus that parasitizes rye causes convulsive ergotism in humans who eat bread made with infested grains. The bizarre behavior of young women who were later convicted of witchcraft in Salem Village, Massachusetts, in 1692 has been attributed to convulsive ergotism.

In this exercise, you will learn about the structure of typical fungi and the characteristics of four important phyla of fungi: Zygomycota, Ascomycota, Basidiomycota, and Deuteromycota. You will see examples of lichens that are associations between fungi and algae. As you observe these examples, consider interesting questions that might be asked about fungi diversity or ecology. You can choose one of these questions to design a simple experiment in Exercise 3.

Lab Study A. Zygote Fungi—Zygomycota

Materials

compound microscope
stereoscopic microscope
cultures of *Rhizopus stolonifer*
  with sporangia
cultures of *Pilobolus crystallinus*
  on demonstration

forceps, ethyl alcohol, alcohol lamp
slides and coverslips
dropper bottles of water with

Introduction

One common organism in the phylum Zygomycota is probably growing in your refrigerator right now. The common bread mold, *Rhizopus stolonifer,* grows on many foods as well as bread. In this lab study, you will observe the structure of this species to see many general fungi characteristics. Fungi are made up of thread-like individual filaments, called **hyphae,** which are organized into the body of the fungus, called the **mycelium.** This filamentous mass secretes enzymes into the substrate and digests food that will then be absorbed into its cells. Cells of fungi have cell walls made of **chitin** combined with other complex carbohydrates, including cellulose. You may recall that chitin is the main component of insect exoskeletons.

Rhizopus stolonifer

Rhizopus reproduces both sexually and asexually. In the zygomycetes (fungi in the phylum Zygomycota), cells of the hyphae are haploid. Hyphae grow over a substrate, for example, a slice of bread, giving the bread a fuzzy appearance. In asexual reproduction, certain hyphae grow upright and develop **sporangia,** round structures, on their tips. Haploid spores develop in the sporangia following mitosis, and when they are mature, they are dispersed through the air. If they fall on a suitable medium, they will absorb water and germinate, growing a new mycelium.

Rhizopus also reproduces sexually when compatible mating types designated as (+) and (−) grow side by side. In this case, (+) and (−) hyphae produce extensions called **gametangia** that fuse forming **zygosporangia.** Within the zygosporangia, haploid nuclei fuse (*karyogamy*) producing diploid nuclei. The diploid nuclei then undergo meiosis. Following meiosis, haploid spores are produced in sporangia borne on filaments that emerge from the zygosporangia (Figure 11).

Pilobolus crystallinus

Pilobolus crystallinus (also called the *fungus gun,* or *shotgun fungus*) is another member of the phylum Zygomycota. This fungus is called a **coprophilous** fungus because it grows on dung. It displays many unusual behaviors, one of which is that it is positively phototropic. Perhaps you can investigate this behavior in Exercise 3. Bold et al. (1980) describe asexual reproduction in *Pilobolus.* This species has sporangia as does *Rhizopus,* but rather than similarly dispersing single spores, in *Pilobolus* the sporangium is forcibly discharged as a unit; the dispersion is tied to moisture and diurnal cycles. In nature, in the early evening the sporangia form; shortly after midnight, a swelling appears below the sporangium. Late the following morning, turgor

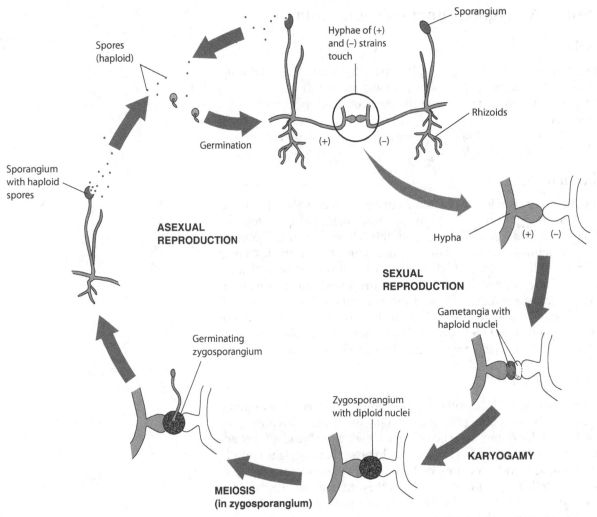

Figure 11.

Rhizopus stolonifer. *Rhizopus* reproduces both sexually by zygosporangia and asexually by sporangia producing asexual spores. In sexual reproduction, (+) and (−) mating types fuse and a zygosporangium with diploid nuclei ultimately results.

pressure causes the swelling to explode, propelling the sporangium as far as 2 meters. The sticky sporangium will adhere to grass leaves and subsequently may be eaten by an animal—horse, cow, or rabbit. The intact sporangia pass through the animal's digestive tract and are excreted, and the spores germinate in the fresh dung.

In this lab study you will investigate *Rhizopus* and observe *Pilobolus* on demonstration.

Procedure

1. Obtain a culture of *Rhizopus* and carry it to your lab station.
2. Examine it using the stereoscopic microscope.
3. Identify the **mycelia, hyphae,** and **sporangia.**
4. Review the life cycle of *Rhizopus* (Figure 11). Locate the structures in this figure that are visible in your culture. Circle the structures involved in asexual reproduction.

5. Using forceps and aseptic technique, remove a small portion of the mycelium with several sporangia and make a wet mount.

6. Examine the hyphae and sporangia using the compound microscope. Are spores visible? How have the spores been produced?

How do the spores compare with the hyphal cells genetically?

How would spores produced by sexual reproduction differ from spores produced asexually?

7. Observe the cultures of *Pilobolus* (Figure 12) growing on rabbit dung agar that are on demonstration.

8. Identify the **sporangia, mycelia,** and **hyphae.** What color are the sporangia and spores?

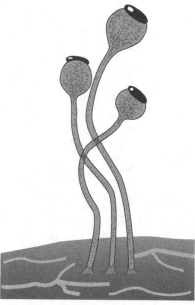

Adapted from illustrations by Miguel Ulloa, Departamento de Botanica, Instituto de Biologia, Universidad Nacional Autonoma de Mexico.

Figure 12.
Pilobolus crystallinus.

Results

1. Review the life cycle of *Rhizopus* and the structures observed in the living culture and compare with Figure 11.

2. Review the structures observed in *Pilobolus* and compare with Figure 12.

Discussion

1. The body form of most fungi, including *Rhizopus,* is a mycelium composed of filamentous hyphae. Using your observations as a basis for your thinking, state why this body form is well adapted to the fungus mode of nutrition.

2. Refer back to the description of *Pilobolus.* Speculate about the adaptive advantage of having a system to propel sporangia, as seen in *Pilobolus.*

Lab Study B. Sac Fungi—Ascomycota

Materials

compound microscope
stereoscopic microscope
dried or preserved *Peziza* specimen

prepared slide of *Peziza* ascocarp
preserved or fresh morels
plastic mounts of ergot in rye
or wheat

Introduction

Fungi in the phylum Ascomycota are called *sac fungi*, or ascopore-producing fungi. This division includes edible fungi, morels, and truffles, but it also includes several deadly plant and animal parasites. For example, chestnut blight and Dutch elm disease have devastated native populations of chestnut and American elm trees. The fungi causing these diseases were introduced into the United States from Asia and Europe. You may have already examined one example of the phylum Ascomycota when you studied meiosis and crossing over in *Sordaria fimicola*.

Sexual reproduction in the ascomycota fungi produces either four or eight haploid **ascospores** after meiosis in an **ascus**. Recall that spores in *Sordaria* form after meiosis within asci. Asci form within a structure called an **ascocarp**. In *Sordaria* the ascocarp, called a *perithecium*, is a closed, spherical structure that develops a pore at the top for spore dispersal. In some species of sac fungi, the asci are borne on open cup-shaped ascocarps called *apothecia* (sing., *apothecium*). In asexual reproduction, spores are produced, but rather than being enclosed within a sporangium as in zygote fungi, the spores, called **conidia**, are produced on the surface of special reproductive hyphae.

Other features of sac fungi also vary. For example, yeasts are ascomycetes, yet they are single-celled organisms. Yeasts most frequently reproduce asexually by **budding**, a process in which small cells form by pinching off the parent cell. When they reproduce sexually, however, they produce asci, each of which produces four or eight spores.

In this lab study, you will examine a slide of the sac fungi *Peziza* and will observe demonstrations of additional examples of Ascomycota.

Procedure

1. Obtain a dried or preserved specimen of *Peziza* (Figure 13a). Notice the open, cup-shaped apothecium, the **ascocarp,** that bears asci within the cup (not visible with the naked eye). Fungi with ascocarps shaped in this fashion are called **cup fungi.** The cup may be supported by a stalk.

2. Examine a prepared slide of *Peziza* using low and intermediate magnifications on the compound microscope. This slide is a section through the ascocarp. Identify **asci.** How many spores are present per ascus? Are they diploid or haploid?

3. Complete the sketch of the ascocarp section that follows, labeling **asci, spores, hyphae,** and **mycelium.**

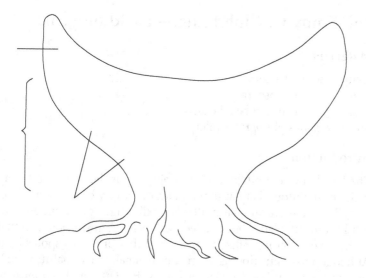

4. Observe the preserved **morels** that are on demonstration (Figure 13b). These fungi resemble mushrooms, but the "cap" is convoluted. Asci are located inside the ridges.

5. Observe demonstrations of the mature inflorescence of wheat or rye grass infected with the ascomycete *Claviceps purpurea,* the **ergot** fungus. The large black structures seen among the grains are the ergot.

Results

Review the structures observed in *Peziza*, morels, and ergot. Modify Figures 13a and 13b to reflect features of your examples not included in these figures. Sketch ergot examples in the margin of your lab manual.

Discussion

What characteristics are common to all sac fungi?

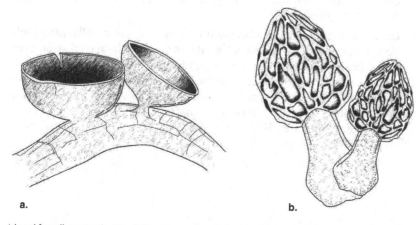

a.   b.

Adapted from illustrations by Miguel Ulloa, Departamento de Botanica, Instituto de Biologia, Universidad Nacional Autonoma de Mexico.

Figure 13.
Examples of sac fungi, phylum Ascomycota. (a) *Peziza* has a cup-shaped ascocarp with asci within the cup. (b) Morels are cup fungi that resemble mushrooms.

Lab Study C. Club Fungi—Basidiomycota

Materials

compound microscope
stereoscopic microscope
fresh, ripe mushroom basidiocarps
prepared slides of *Coprinus* pileus sections

Introduction

The Basidiomycota phylum (club fungi, or basidiospore-producing fungi) includes the fungi that cause the plant diseases wheat rust and corn smut as well as the more familiar puffballs, shelf fungi, and edible and nonedible mushrooms (the latter often called *toadstools*). A mushroom is actually a reproductive structure called a basidiocarp that produces spores by meiosis. Although most mushrooms are relatively small when mature, one basidiocarp in the Royal Botanic Gardens, Kew, England, in 1996 measured 146 cm (57 inches wide) and weighed 284 kg (625 pounds)! Basidiocarps grow upward from an underground mycelial mass. When they form around the rim of the mass, a "fairy ring" of mushrooms appears. In asexual reproduction, conidia form by mitosis. In this lab study, you will study mushrooms and learn some features of their life cycle.

Procedure

1. Obtain a fresh mushroom, a **basidiocarp,** and identify its parts: The stalk is the **stipe;** the cap is the **pileus.** Look under the cap and identify **gills.** Spores form on the surface of the gills. Examine the gills with the stereoscopic microscope. Do you see spores? Children often make spore prints in scouts or in elementary school by placing a ripe mushroom pileus with the gill side down on a piece of white paper for several hours, allowing the spores to drop to the paper. Scientists use similar spore prints to accurately identify mushrooms.

2. Label the parts of the mushrooms in Figure 14a.

3. Obtain a prepared slide of a section through the pileus of *Coprinus* or another mushroom. Observe it on the compound microscope using low and then intermediate powers. Is your slide a cross section or a longitudinal section through the pileus? Make a sketch in the lab manual margin indicating the plane of your section through the basidiocarp. Compare your section with the fresh mushroom you have just studied and with Figure 14b.

4. Using the prepared slide, observe the surface of several gills using high power. Spores are produced at the tips of small club-shaped structures called **basidia.** Locate a basidium and focus carefully on its end. Here you may see four knoblike protuberances. Each protuberance has a haploid nucleus that formed following meiosis, and each becomes a **basidiospore.** When the spores are mature, they are discharged from the basidium and are dispersed by the wind.

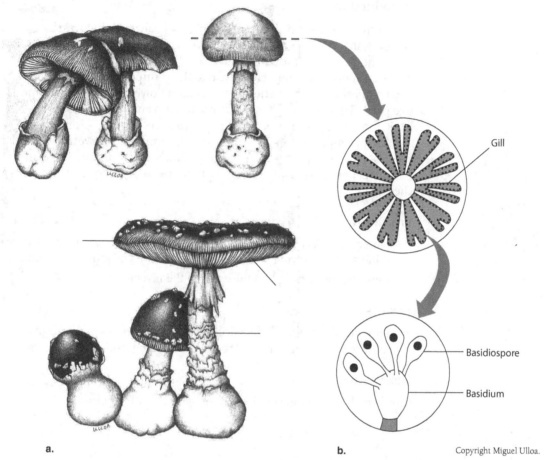

a.   b.   Copyright Miguel Ulloa.

Figure 14.
Club fungi, phylum Basidiomycota. (a) Mushrooms, or basidiocarps, each consisting of a cap, the pileus; and a stalk, the stipe. (b) A section through the gills on a whole basidiocarp reveals basidia and basidiospores.

Results

Review the structures observed and label Figure 14a. Modify the figure to include features observed in your materials that differ from the figure.

Discussion

State the characteristics shared by all Basidiomycota.

Lab Study D. Imperfect Fungi—Deuteromycota

Materials

cultures of *Penicillium* on demonstration
Roquefort cheese on demonstration

Introduction

Most fungi are classified based on their sexual reproductive structures; however, many fungi (as far as is known) reproduce only vegetatively. Because the sexual reproductive stages of these fungi do not exist or have not been found, they are called **asexual**, or **imperfect fungi** (following the botanical use of "imperfect" to indicate a flower lacking one reproductive part). This group is of interest because several human diseases—athlete's foot, ringworm, and candida "yeast" infections—are caused by species of imperfect fungi. Also in this group are several beneficial species—for example, one species of *Penicillium* that produces the antibiotic penicillin and another that is used to make Roquefort and blue cheeses.

Procedure

1. Observe the *Penicillium* on demonstration. You may have observed something similar growing on oranges or other foods in your refrigerator.
2. Describe the texture and the color of the mycelium.

Results

Sketch your observations of *Penicillium* in the margin of your lab manual. Note any features that may be important in distinguishing this organism.

Discussion

Compare the appearance of *Penicillium* with that of *Rhizopus*.

Lab Study E. Lichens

Materials

examples of foliose, crustose, and fruticose lichens on demonstration

Introduction

Lichens are symbiotic associations between fungi and usually algae or cyanobacteria forming a body that can be consistently recognized. The fungal component is usually a sac fungus or a club fungus. The lichen body, called a **thallus**, varies in shape and colors, depending on the species of the components. Reproductive structures can be bright red or pink or green. Photosynthesis in the algae provides nutrients for the fungus, and the fungus provides a moist environment for the algae or cyanobacterium. Because lichens can survive extremely harsh environments, they are often the first organisms to colonize a newly exposed environment such as volcanic flow or rock outcrops, and they play a role in soil formation.

Procedure

Observe the demonstrations of different lichen types: those with a leafy thallus (**foliose**), a crustlike thallus (**crustose**), or a branching, cylindrical

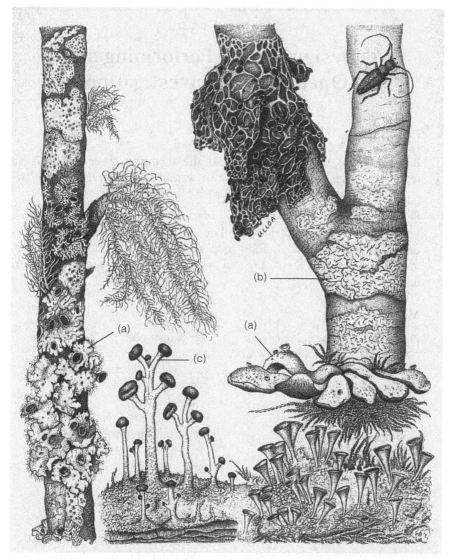

Figure 15.
Lichen types. Lichens may have (a) a leafy thallus (foliose), (b) a crustlike thallus (crustose), or (c) a cylindrical thallus (fruticose).

Copyright Miguel Ulloa.

thallus (**fruticose**) (Figure 15). Look for cup-shaped or club-like reproductive structures produced by the fungal component of the lichen.

Results

1. Sketch the lichens on demonstration in the margins of your lab manual.
2. Label any visible reproductive structures, and, if possible, indicate if the fungal component is a sac fungus or a club fungus.
3. Identify and label each according to lichen type.

Discussion

Imagine that you are the first scientist to observe a lichen microscopically. What observations would lead you to conclude that the lichen is composed of a fungus and an alga?

EXERCISE 3

Designing and Performing an Open-Inquiry Investigation

Introduction

In this exercise, you will choose one of the organisms observed in this lab topic and design a simple experiment answering a question about its behavior, growth patterns, or interactions with other species.

Be ready to assign tasks to members of your lab team. Be sure that everyone understands the techniques that will be used. Your experiment will be successful only if you plan carefully, cooperate with your team members, perform lab techniques accurately and systematically, and record and report data accurately.

Materials

protozoa and algae cultures
cultures of slime molds *Physarum,*
  Didymium, Dictyostelium
cultures of *Pilobolus crystallinus,*
  Rhizopus, Penicillium
sterile agar plates to grow
  each species
sterile agar with oat flakes
sterile agar with sugar
sterile agar with albumin

sterile agar with pH 6, 7, or 8
aluminum foil
various breads from the health
  food store—wheat, rye, corn,
  potato, rice
bread with preservatives
sterilized dung from various
  animals
mycorrhizae inoculate

Procedure

1. Choose a question from this list to investigate or choose a question from your own observations. *Write your question in the margin of your lab manual.*

   a. Will varying the molarity of the culture medium change the rate of contractile vacuole formation in paramecia?

   b. Do plasmodia of the same species of slime mold unite when growing on the same agar plate? How about different species of slime mold?

   c. Do slime mold plasmodia demonstrate chemotaxis (response to chemical stimuli such as food molecules) or phototaxis (response to light)?

   d. What happens to slime molds if grown in different temperatures?

   e. Do the same fungi grow on different varieties of bread?

   f. How effective are preservatives in preventing fungal growth on foods?

   g. Is *Pilobolus* phototaxic? What about other fungi?

   h. Does succession take place in dung cultures of fungi? Refer to the milk bacteria succession study and design a similar experiment to investigate this phenomenon in fungi growing on dung.

  i. Is there a difference in the growth of plants growing with and without mycorrhizae?

  j. Can the growth of fungi be altered by supplying different nutrients (e.g., sugar or albumin) in agar culture?

2. Formulate a testable hypothesis.

 Hypothesis:

3. Summarize the experiment. (Use separate paper.)

4. Predict the results of your experiment based on your hypothesis.

 Prediction: (If/then)

5. Outline the procedures used in the experiment.

  a. On a separate sheet of paper, list in numerical order each exact step of your procedure.

  b. Remember to include the number of replicates (usually a minimum of five), levels of treatment, appropriate time intervals, and controls for each procedure.

  c. If you have an idea for an experiment that requires materials other than those provided, ask your laboratory instructor about availability. If possible, additional supplies will be provided.

  d. When carrying out an experiment, remember to quantify your measurements when possible.

6. Perform the experiment, making observations and collecting data for analysis.

7. **Record observations and data** on a separate sheet of paper. Design tables and graphs, at least one of each. Be thorough when collecting data. Do not just write down numbers, but record what they mean as well. Do not rely on your memory for information that you will need when reporting your results.

8. **Prepare your discussion.** Discuss your results in light of your hypothesis.

  a. Review your hypothesis. Review your results (tables and graphs). Do your results support or falsify your hypothesis? Explain your answer, using data for support.

  b. Review your prediction. Did your results correspond to the prediction you made? If not, explain how your results are different from your predictions, and why this might have occurred.

  c. If you had problems with the procedure or questionable results, explain how they might have influenced your conclusion.

d. If you had an opportunity to repeat and expand this experiment to make your results more convincing, what would you do?

e. Summarize the conclusion you have drawn from your results.

9. **Be prepared to report your results to the class.** Prepare to persuade your fellow scientists that your experimental design is sound and that your results support your conclusions.

10. If your instructor requires it, **submit a written laboratory report** in the form of a scientific paper. Keep in mind that although you have performed the experiments as a team, you must turn in a lab report of *your original writing.* Your tables and figures may be similar to those of your team members, but your paper must be the product of your own literature search and creative thinking.

Questions for Review

1. Complete Table 5 comparing characteristics of all protists investigated in Exercise 1.

2. Complete Table 6 comparing characteristics of fungi (Exercise 2).

3. Compare spore formation in sac fungi and club fungi.

4. Using observations of pigments present, body form, and distinguishing characteristics of the three groups of macroscopic green, brown, and red algae, speculate about where they might be most commonly found in ocean waters.

Table 5
Comparison of Protists Studied in Exercise 1

Group (Clade)	Example(s)	Characteristics	Ecological Role	Economic Importance
Euglenozoans	*Trypanosoma levisi*			
Alveolates	Paramecia			
	Dinoflagellates			
Stramenopiles	Diatoms			
	Brown algae			
Foraminiferans and Radiolarians	Foraminiferans			
	Radiolarians			
Amoebozoans	Amoeba			
	Physarum			
Rhodophyta	Red algae			
Chlorophyta	Green algae: *Spirogyra, Ulva Chara*			

Table 6
Comparison of Fungi by Major Features

Phylum	Example(s)	Sexual Reproductive Structures	Asexual Reproductive Structures
Zygomycota (Zygote Fungi)			
Ascomycota (Sac Fungi)			
Basidiomycota (Club Fungi)			
Deuteromycota (Imperfect Fungi)			

Applying Your Knowledge

1. Scientists are concerned that the depletion of the ozone layer will result in a reduction of populations of marine algae such as diatoms and dinoflagellates. Recall the ecological role of these organisms and comment on the validity of this concern.

2. Imagine an ecosystem with no fungi. How would it be modified?

3. Speculate about a possible evolutionary advantage to the *fungus* for the following:

   a. *Penicillium* makes and secretes an antibiotic.

   b. *Ergot* fungus (parasitizes rye grain) produces a chemical that is toxic to animals.

4. In 1950 the living world was classified simply into two kingdoms: plants and animals. More recently, scientists developed the five-kingdom system of classification: plants, animals, monerans, protists, and fungi. In 2000 there was a general consensus among scientists that three domains with more than five kingdoms was a better system for classifying the diversity of life on Earth. However, there is still no consensus on the number of kingdoms or the clustering of organisms that best represents their evolutionary relationships. Using the protists studied in this lab topic, explain why the classification of this diverse group in particular is problematic. How is solving the problem of organizing protistan diversity a model for understanding the process of science?

 Student Media Activities and Investigations

Activities—Ch 28: Tentative Phylogeny of Eukaryotes; Ch. 31: Fungal Reproduction and Nutrition; Fungal Life Cycles.
Investigation—Ch. 28: What Kinds of Protists Do Various Habitats Support? Ch. 31: How Does the Fungus *Pilobolus* Succeed as a Decomposer?
www.masteringbio.com

References

Ahmadjian, V. "Lichens Are More Important Than You Think." *BioScience*, 1995, vol. 45, p. 124.

Alexopoulos, C., C. Mims, and M. Blackwell. *Introductory Mycology*, 4th ed. New York: John Wiley and Sons, Inc., 1996.

Anderson, R. "What to Do with Protists?" *Australian Systematic Botany*, 1998, vol. 11, p. 185.

Bold, H., C. J. Alexopoulos, and T. Delevoryas. *Morphology of Plants and Fungi*. New York: Harper & Row, 1980, p. 654.

Campbell, N., and J. Reece. *Biology*, 8th ed. San Francisco, CA: Benjamin Cummings, 2008.

Crowder, W. "Marvels of Mycetozoa." *National Geographic Magazine*, 1926, vol. 49, pp. 421–443.

Doolittle, W. F. "Uprooting the Tree of Life." *Scientific American*, 2000, vol. 282, pp. 90–95.

Litten, W. "The Most Poisonous Mushrooms." *Scientific American*, 1975, vol. 232.

Websites

Protist Image Data. Excellent page links:
http://megasun.bch.umontreal.ca/protists/protists.html

Links to pictures of red, brown, and green algae:
http://www.sonoma.edu/biology/algae/algae.html

Seaweeds:
http://www.botany.uwc.ac.za/Envfacts/seaweeds/

The Tree of Life web project—a collaborative effort of biologists from around the world to present information on diversity and phylogeny of organisms:
http://tolweb.org/tree/phylogeny

Mycological Resources on the Internet:
http://mycology.cornell.edu

See an amoeba video and find interesting information on amoebas:
http://www.microscopy.fsu.edu/moviegallery/pondscum/protozoa/amoeba/

Lichens:
www.lichen.com

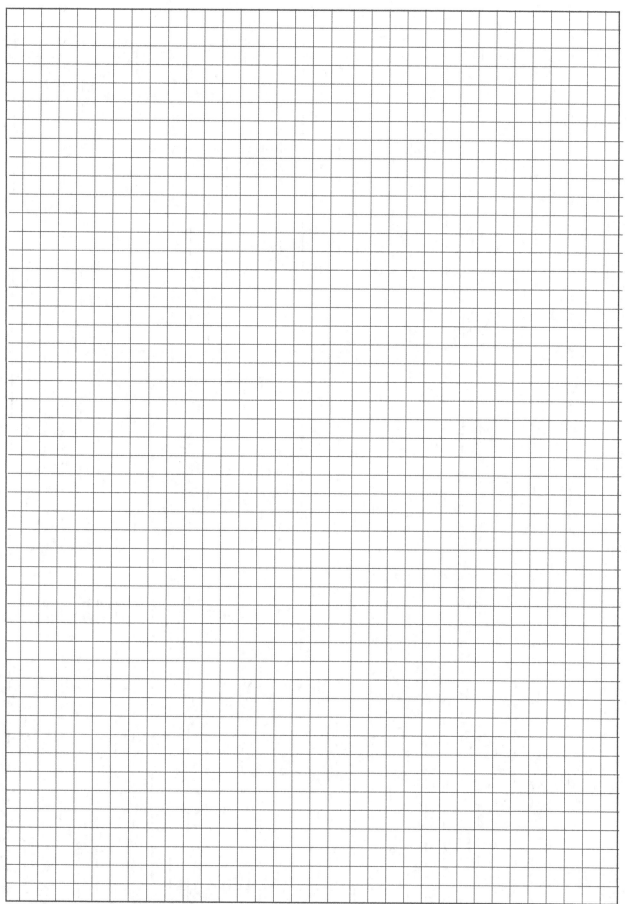

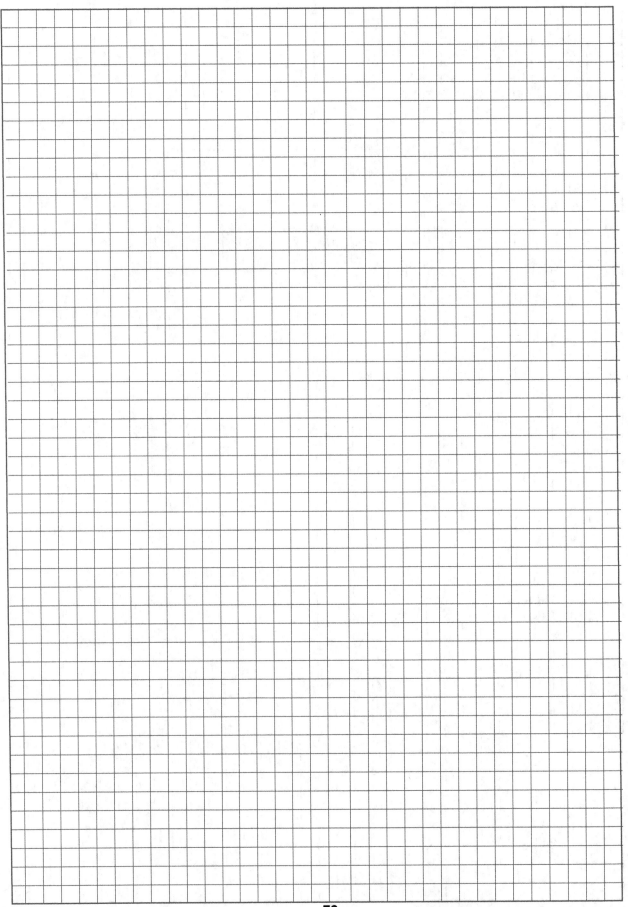

Plant Diversity: Nonvascular Plants (Bryophytes) and Seedless Vascular Plants

Laboratory Objectives

After completing this lab topic, you should be able to:

1. Describe the distinguishing characteristics of nonvascular plants and seedless vascular plants.

2. Discuss the ancestral and derived features of nonvascular plants and seedless vascular plants relative to their adaptations to the land environment.

3. Recognize and identify representative members of each phylum of nonvascular plants and seedless vascular plants.

4. Describe the general life cycle and alternation of generations in the nonvascular plants and the seedless vascular plants, and discuss the differences between the life cycles of the two groups of plants using examples.

5. Identify fossil members and their extant counterparts in the seedless vascular plants.

6. Describe homospory and heterospory, including the differences in spores and gametophytes.

7. Discuss the ecological role and economic importance of these groups of plants.

Introduction

In the history of life on Earth, one of the most revolutionary events was the colonization of land, first by plants, then by animals. Evidence from comparisons of extant land plants and phyla of algae suggests that the first land plants were related to the green algae. These first colonists are thought to be most similar to the living, branched, multicellular green alga *Chara*. Once these simple ancestral plants arrived on land over 475 million years ago, they faced new and extreme challenges in their physical environment. Only individuals that were able to survive the variations in temperature, moisture, gravitational forces, and substrate would thrive. Out of this enormous selective regime would come new and different adaptations and new and different life forms: the land plants.

Land plants generally have complex, multicellular plant bodies that are specialized for a variety of functions. Land plants in the Kingdom **Plantae** produce embryos and have evolved specialized structures for protection of the vulnerable stages of sexual reproduction. The plant body is often covered

From *Investigating Biology Laboratory Manual,* Sixth Edition, Judith G. Morgan and M. Eloise Brown Carter. Copyright © 2008 by Pearson Education, Inc. Published by Benjamin Cummings, Inc. All rights reserved.

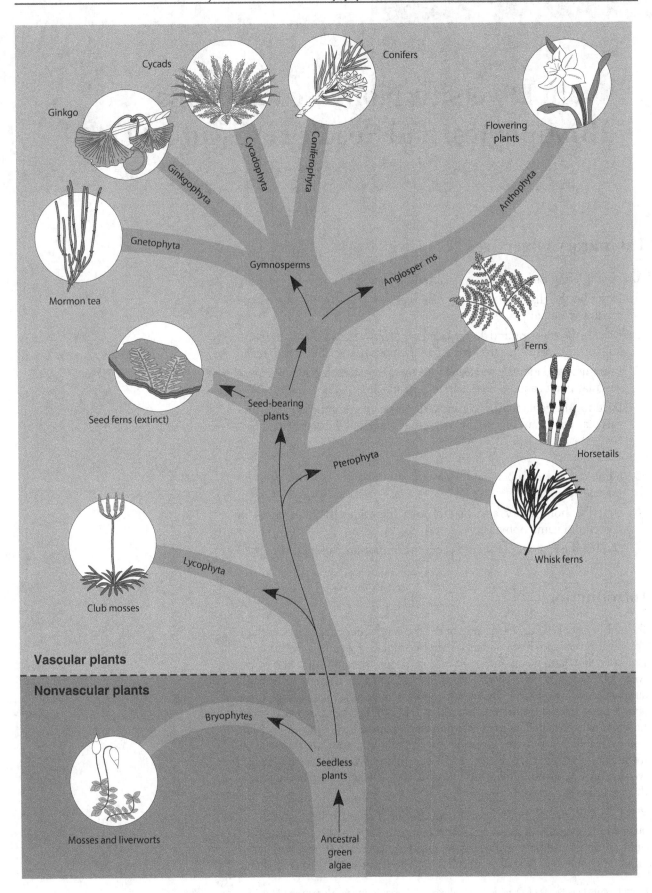

Table 1
Classification of Land Plants

Classification	Common Name	Illustration
Nonvascular Plants (Bryophytes)		
Phylum Bryophyta	Mosses	
Phylum Hepatophyta	Liverworts	
Phylum Anthocerophyta	Hornworts	
Vascular Plants		
Seedless Plants		
Phylum Lycophyta	Club mosses	
Phylum Pterophyta	Ferns, horsetails, whisk ferns	
Seed Plants		
Gymnosperms		
Phylum Coniferophyta	Conifers	
Phylum Cycadophyta	Cycads	
Phylum Ginkgophyta	Ginkgo	
Phylum Gnetophyta	Mormon tea	
Angiosperms		
Phylum Anthophyta	Flowering plants	

with a waxy cuticle that prevents desiccation. However, the waxy covering also prevents gas exchange, a problem solved by the presence of openings called **stomata** (sing., **stoma**). Some land plants have developed vascular tissue for efficient movement of materials throughout these complex bodies, which are no longer bathed in water. As described in the following section, the reproductive cycles and reproductive structures of these plants are also adapted to the land environment.

You will be investigating the diversity of land plants (Table 1 and Figure 1), some of which will be familiar to you (flowering plants, pine trees, and ferns) and some of which you may never have seen before (whisk ferns, horsetails, and liverworts). *To maintain your perspective in the face of all this*

(☜) **Figure 1.**

Evolution of land plants. The nonvascular plants and vascular plants probably evolved from ancestral green algae over 475 million years ago. Seedless vascular plants dominated Earth 300 million years ago, and representatives of two phyla have survived until the present. Seed plants replaced the seedless plants as the dominant land plants, and today flowering plants are the most diverse and successful group in an amazing variety of habitats. The representatives studied in Plant Diversity labs are indicated.

diversity—and to remember the major themes of these labs—bear in mind the following questions.

1. What are the special adaptations of these plants to the land environment?
2. How are specialized plant structures related to functions in the land environment?
3. What are the major trends in the plant kingdom as plant life evolved over the past 500 million years?
4. In particular, how has the fundamental reproductive cycle of alternation of generations been modified in successive groups of plants?

Plant Life Cycles

All land plants have a common sexual reproductive life cycle called **alternation of generations,** in which plants alternate between a haploid **gametophyte** generation and a diploid **sporophyte** generation (Figure 2). In living land plants, these two generations differ in their morphology, but they are still the same species. In all land plants except the bryophytes (mosses and liverworts), the diploid sporophyte generation is the dominant (more conspicuous) generation.

The essential features in the alternation of generations life cycle beginning with the sporophyte are:

- The diploid sporophyte undergoes meiosis to produce haploid **spores** in a protective, nonreproductive jacket of cells called the **sporangium**.
- Dividing by mitosis the spores germinate to produce the haploid gametophyte.

Figure 2.
Alternation of generations. In this life cycle, a diploid sporophyte plant alternates with a haploid gametophyte plant. Note that haploid spores are produced on the sporophyte by meiosis, and haploid gametes are produced in the gametophyte by mitosis. *Using a colored pencil, indicate the structures that are haploid, and with another color, note the structures that are diploid.*

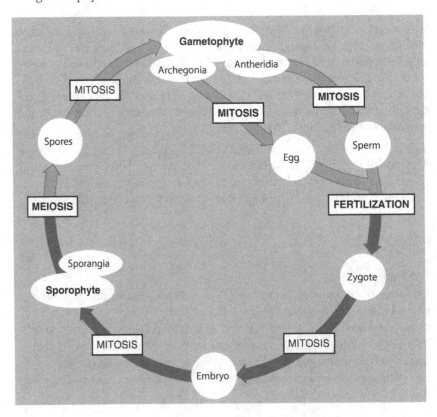

- The gametophyte produces **gametes** inside a jacket of cells forming **gametangia** (sing., **gamtangium**).
- **Eggs** are produced by mitosis in **archegonia** (sing., **archegonium**), and **sperm** are produced in **antheridia** (sing., **anteridium**).
- The gametes fuse (**fertilization**) usually by entrance of the sperm into the archegonium, forming a diploid **zygote**, the first stage of the diploid sporophyte generation.

Note that both gametes and spores are haploid in this life cycle. Unlike the animal life cycle, *the plant life cycle produces gametes by mitosis; spores are produced by meiosis.* The difference between these two cells is that gametes fuse with other gametes to form the zygote and restore the diploid number, while spores germinate to form a new haploid gametophyte plant.

Review the generalized diagram of this life cycle in Figure 2. *Using colored pencils, note the structures that are diploid and those that are haploid.* As you become familiar with variations of this life cycle through specific examples, you will want to continue referring to this general model for review.

Major trends in the evolution of this life cycle include the increased importance of the sporophyte as the photosynthetic and persistent plant that dominates the life cycle; the reduction and protection of the gametophyte within the body of the sporophyte; and the evolution of seeds and then flowers.

Nonvascular Plants (Bryophytes) and Seedless Vascular Plants

In this lab topic, terrestrial plants will be used to illustrate how life has undergone dramatic changes during the past 500 million years. Not long after the transition to land, plants diverged into at least two separate lineages. One gave rise to the bryophytes, a group of nonvascular plants, including the mosses, and the other to the vascular plants (see Figure 1). Nonvascular bryophytes first appear in the fossil record dating over 420 million years ago and remain unchanged, whereas the vascular plants have undergone enormous diversification. As you review the evolution of land plants, refer to the geological time chart for an overview of the history of life on Earth (Figure 3, on the next page).

EXERCISE 1
Nonvascular Plants (Bryophytes)

The nonvascular plants are composed of three phyla of related plants that share some key characteristics and include mosses (Bryophyta) and liverworts (Hepatophyta). The third phylum, hornworts (Anthocerophyta), will not be seen in lab. (See again Figure 1 and Table 1.) The term *bryophytes* does not refer to a taxonomic category; rather, bryophytes are an ancient group of nonvascular plants that share a common ancestor, appear to have evolved into several different groups independently, and did not give rise to any other living groups of plants. They are small plants generally lacking vascular tissue (specialized cells for the transport of material), although

Years Ago (millions)	Era	Period	Epoch	Life on Earth
	CENOZOIC	Quaternary	Recent	• Origin of agriculture and artificial selection; H. sapiens
			Pleistocene	
1.8		Tertiary		
			Pliocene	• Large carnivores; hominoid apes
5			Miocene	• Forests dwindle; grassland spreads
23			Oligocene	• Anthropoid apes
35			Eocene	• Diversification of mammals and flowering plants
57			Paleocene	• Specialized flowers; sophisticated pollinators and seed distributors
65	**MESOZOIC**	Cretaceous		• Flowering plants established and diversified; many modern families present; extinction of many dinosaurs
145		Jurassic		• Origin of birds; reptiles dominant; cycads and ferns abundant; first modern conifers and immediate ancestors of flowering plants
208		Triassic		• First dinosaurs and mammals; forests of gymnosperms and ferns; cycads
245	**PALEOZOIC**	Permian		• Diversification of gymnosperms; origin of reptiles; amphibians dominant
290		Carboniferous		• First treelike plants; giant woody lycopods and sphenopsids form extensive forests in swampy areas; evolution of early seeds (seed ferns) and first stages of leaves
363		Devonian		• Diversification of vascular plants; sharks and fishes dominant in the oceans
409		Silurian		• First vascular plants
439		Ordovician		• Diversification of algae and plants colonize land
510		Cambrian		• Diversification of major animal phyla
570	**PRECAMBRIAN**	Precambrian		• Origin of bacteria, archaea, and eukaryotes
	Earth is about 4.6 billion years old			

water-conducting tubes appear to be present in some mosses. (However, these tubes may be unrelated to the vascular tissue in vascular plants.) The life cycle for the bryophytes differs from all other land plants because the gametophyte is the dominant and conspicuous plant. Because bryophytes are nonvascular, they are restricted to moist habitats for their reproductive cycle and have never attained the size and importance of other groups of plants. The gametophyte plants remain close to the ground, enabling the motile sperm to swim from the antheridium to the archegonium and fertilize the egg. They have a cuticle but lack stomata on the surface of the gametophyte **thallus** (plant body), which is not organized into roots, stems, and leaves. Stomata are present on the sporophyte in some mosses and hornworts.

Bryophytes are not important economically, with the exception of sphagnum moss, which in its harvested and dried form is known as *peat moss*. Peat moss is absorbent, has an antibacterial agent, and was reportedly once used as bandages and diapers. Today peat moss is used in the horticultural industry, and dried peat is burned as fuel in some parts of the world. Peat lands cover more than one percent of the Earth's surface and store 400 billion metric tons of organic carbon. Harvesting and burning peat releases CO_2 to the atmosphere, thus contributing to changes in the global carbon cycle.

Lab Study A. Bryophyta: Mosses

Materials

living examples of mosses
prepared slides of *Mnium* archegonia and antheridia
colored pencils

Introduction

The mosses are the most common group of nonvascular plants, occurring primarily in moist environments but also found in dry habitats that are periodically wet. Refer to Figure 4 on the next page as you investigate the moss life cycle, which is representative of the bryophytes.

Procedure

1. Examine living colonies of mosses on demonstration. Usually you will find the two generations, gametophyte and sporophyte, growing together.
2. Identify the leafy **gametophytes** and the dependent **sporophytes**, which appear as elongated structures growing above them. Tug gently at the sporophyte and notice that it is attached to the gametophyte. Recall that the sporophyte develops and matures while attached to the gametophyte and receives its moisture and nutrients from the gametophyte.

(☜) **Figure 3.**
Geological time chart. The history of life can be organized into time periods that reflect changes in the physical and biological environment. Refer to this table as you review the evolution of land plants in the Plant Diversity labs.

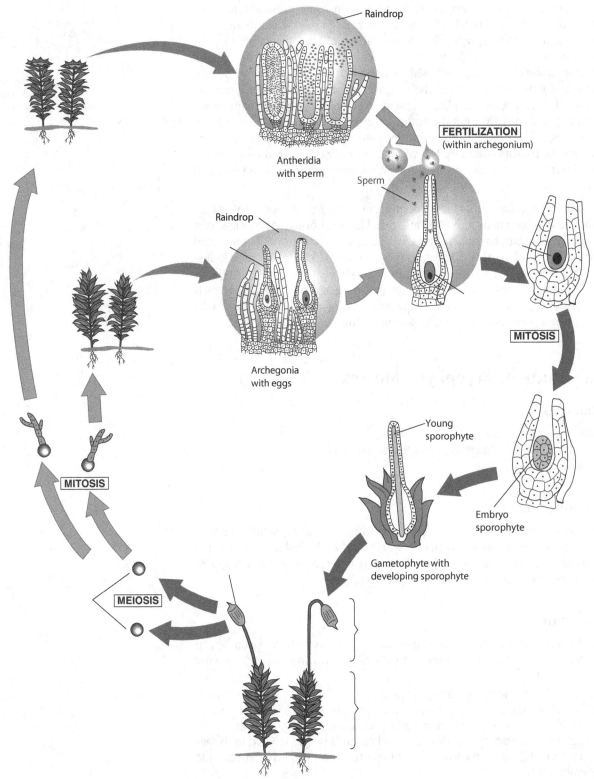

Figure 4.

Moss life cycle. The leafy moss plant is the gametophyte, and the sporophyte is dependent on it, deriving its water and nutrients from the body of the gametophyte. Review this variation of alternation of generations and label the structures described in Lab Study A. *Using colored pencils, highlight the haploid and diploid structures in different colors. Circle the processes of mitosis and meiosis.*

3. The gametes are produced by the gametophyte in **gametangia** *by mitosis.* Gametangia protect the gametes but are not readily visible without a microscope. Observe under the microscope's low-power lens prepared slides containing long sections of heads of the unisex moss *Mnium,* which contain the gametangia. One slide has been selected to show the **antheridia** (male); the other is a rosette of **archegonia** (female). Sperm-forming tissue will be visible inside the antheridia. On the archegonial slide, look for an archegonium. The moss archegonium has a very long neck and rounded base. It will be difficult to find an entire archegonium in any one section. Search for a single-celled **egg** in the base of the archegonium.

4. Refer to Figure 4 as you follow the steps of fertilization through formation of the gametophyte in the next generation. The sperm swim through a film of water to the archegonium and swim down the neck to the egg, where fertilization takes place. The diploid zygote divides by mitosis and develops into an embryonic sporophyte within the archegonium. As the sporophyte matures, it grows out of the gametophyte but remains attached, deriving water and nutrients from the gametophyte body. **Spores** develop *by meiosis* in the **sporangium** at the end of the sporophyte. The spores are discharged from the sporangium and in a favorable environment develop into new gametophytes.

Results

1. Review the structures and processes observed and then label the moss life cycle diagram in Figure 4.
2. Using colored pencils, indicate if structures are haploid or diploid and circle the processes of mitosis and meiosis.

Discussion

Refer to Figure 2, the generalized diagram of the plant life cycle.

1. Are the spores produced by the moss sporophyte formed by meiosis or mitosis? Are they haploid or diploid?

2. Do the spores belong to the gametophyte or sporophyte generation?

3. Are the gametes haploid or diploid? Are they produced by meiosis or mitosis?

4. Is the dominant generation for the mosses the gametophyte or the sporophyte?

5. Can you suggest any ecological role for mosses?

6. What feature of the life cycle differs for bryophytes compared with all other land plants?

Lab Study B. Hepatophyta: Liverworts

Materials

living liverworts

Introduction

Liverworts are so named because their bodies are flattened and lobed. Early herbalists believed that these plants were beneficial in the treatment of liver disorders. Although less common than mosses, liverworts can be found along streams on moist rocks, but because of their small size, you must look closely to locate them.

Procedure

Examine examples of liverworts on demonstration. Liverworts have a flat **thallus** (plant body). Note the **rhizoids,** rootlike extensions on the lower surface, that primarily anchor plants. Observe the **pores** on the surface of the leaflike thallus. These openings function in gas exchange; however, they are always open since they lack guard cells. On the upper surface of the thallus you should see circular cups called **gemmae cups,** which contain flat disks of green tissue called **gemmae.** The gemmae are washed out of the cups when it rains, and they grow into new, genetically identical liverworts.

Results

Sketch the overall structure of the liverwort in the margin of your laboratory manual. Label structures where appropriate.

Discussion

1. Is the plant you observed the gametophyte or sporophyte?

2. Are the gemmae responsible for asexual or sexual reproduction? Explain.

3. Why are these plants, like most bryophytes, restricted to moist habitats, and why are they always small?

4. In this lab topic, you are asked to complete tables that summarize features advantageous to the adaptation of plant groups to the land environment. You may be asked to compare these derived features with others that have changed little (ancestral) in the evolution of land plants. For example, for nonvascular plants, motile sperm might be considered an ancestral feature, while the cuticle would be considered derived.

Complete Table 2, relating the features of nonvascular plants to their success in the land environment. Refer to the lab topic introduction for assistance.

Table 2
Ancestral and Derived Features of Nonvascular Plants
as They Relate to Adaptation to Land

Ancestral Features	Derived Features

EXERCISE 2
Seedless Vascular Plants

Seedless, terrestrial plants are analogous to the first terrestrial vertebrate animals, the amphibians, in their dependence on water for external fertilization and development of the unprotected, free-living embryo. Both groups were important in the Paleozoic era but have undergone a steady decline in importance since that time. Seedless plants were well suited for life in the vast swampy areas that covered large areas of the Earth in the Carboniferous period but were not suited for the drier areas of the Earth at that time or for later climatic changes that caused the vast swamps to decline and disappear. The fossilized remains of the swamp forests are the coal deposits of today (Figure 3 and Figure 7).

Although living representatives of the seedless vascular plants have survived for millions of years, their limited adaptations to the land environment have restricted their range. All seedless vascular plants have vascular tissue, which is specialized for conducting water, nutrients, and photosynthetic products. Their life cycle is a variation of alternation of generations, in which the sporophyte is the dominant plant; the gametophyte is usually independent of the sporophyte. These plants generally have well developed leaves and roots, stomata and structural support tissue. However, since they still retain the ancestral feature of motile sperm that require water for fertilization, the gametophyte is small and restricted to moist habitats.

Economically, the only important members of this group are the ferns, a significant horticultural resource.

The phyla included in the seedless vascular plants are Lycophyta and Pterophyta (see again Table 1 and Figure 1).

The living examples of lycophytes are small club mosses, spike mosses, and quillworts. (Though named "mosses," these plants have vascular tissue and therefore are not true mosses.) The pterophytes include ferns, horsetails, and whisk ferns, that are remarkably different in overall appearance. Current evidence from molecular biology indicates that these diverse plants share a common ancestor and should all be included in the phylum Pterophyta. This evidence also suggests that pterophytes are more closely related to seed plants than they are to lycophytes.

Lab Study A. Lycophyta: Club Mosses

Materials

living *Selaginella* and *Lycopodium*
preserved *Selaginella* with microsporangia and megasporangia
prepared slide of *Selaginella* strobilus, l.s.

Introduction

Living members of Lycophyta are usually found in moist habitats, including bogs and streamsides. However, one species of *Selaginella*, the resurrection plant, inhabits deserts. It remains dormant throughout periods of low rainfall, but then comes to life—resurrects—when it rains. During the Carboniferous period, lycophytes were not inconspicuous parts of the flora but rather formed the forest canopy; they were the ecological equivalent of today's oaks, hickories, and pines (Figure 7).

Nonvascular plants and most seedless vascular plants produce one type of spore (**homospory**), which gives rise to the gametophyte by mitosis. One advanced feature occasionally seen in seedless vascular plants is the production of two kinds of spores (**heterospory**). Large spores called **megaspores** divide by mitosis to produce the female gametophyte. The numerous small spores, **microspores,** produce the male gametophytes by mitosis. Heterospory and separate male and female gametophytes, as seen in *Selaginella,* are unusual in seedless vascular plants, but characteristic of seed-producing vascular plants.

Procedure

1. Examine living club mosses, *Selaginella* and *Lycopodium*. Are they dichotomously branched? (The branches would split in two, appearing to form a Y.) Locate sporangia, which may be present either clustered at the end of the leafy stem tips, forming **strobili,** or **cones,** or dispersed along the leafy stems. Note that these plants have small leaves, or bracts, along the stem.

2. Examine preserved strobili of *Selaginella*. Observe the round sporangia clustered in sporophylls (leaflike structures) at the tip of the stem (Figure 5a). These sporangia contain either four megaspores or numerous microspores. Can you observe any differences in the sporangia or spores?

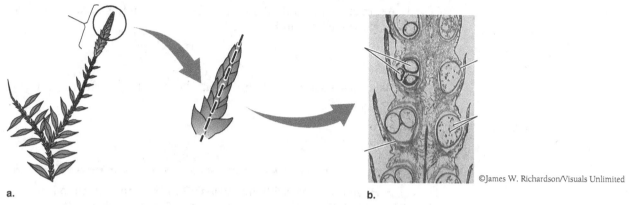

a. b.

©James W. Richardson/Visuals Unlimited

Figure 5.
Selaginella. (a) The leafy plant is the sporophyte. The sporangia are clustered at the tips in strobili. (b) Photomicrograph of a longitudinal section through the strobilus of *Selaginella.*

3. Observe the prepared slide of a long section through the strobilus of *Selaginella.* Begin your observations at low power. Are both microspores and megaspores visible on this slide?

   How can you distinguish these spores?

4. Identify the **strobilus, microsporangium, microspores, megasporangium,** and **megaspores** and label Figure 5.

Results

1. Sketch the overall structure of the club mosses in the margin of your lab manual. Label structures where appropriate.
2. Review Figure 5 of *Selaginella.* Using a colored pencil, highlight the structures that are haploid and part of the gametophyte generation.

Discussion

1. Are these leafy plants part of the sporophyte or the gametophyte generation? Do you have any evidence to support your answer?

2. What features would you look for to determine if this were a seedless vascular plant?

3. Are microspores and megaspores produced by mitosis or meiosis? (Review the life cycle in Figure 2.)

4. Will megaspores divide to form the female gametophyte or the sporophyte?

 Having trouble with life cycles? Return to the introduction and review the generalized life cycle in Figure 2. Reread the introduction to the study of seedless vascular plants. The key to success is to determine where meiosis occurs and to remember the ploidal level for the gametophyte and the sporophyte.

Lab Study B. Pterophyta: Ferns, Horsetails, and Whisk Ferns

Materials

living and/or preserved horsetails (*Equisetum*)
living and/or preserved whisk ferns (*Psilotum*)
living ferns

Introduction

If a time machine could take us back 400 million years to the Silurian period, we would find that vertebrate animals were confined to the seas, and early vascular plants had begun to diversify on land (Figure 3). By the Carboniferous period, ferns, horsetails, and whisk ferns grew alongside the lycophytes. Until recently, these three groups of seedless vascular plants were placed in separate phyla: Pterophyta (ferns), Sphenophyta (horsetails), and Psilophyta (whisk ferns). Strong evidence from molecular biology now reveals a close relationship among these three groups, supporting a common ancestor for the group and their placement in one phylum, Pterophyta.

Psilophytes (**whisk ferns**) are diminutive, dichotomously branched (repeated Y branches), photosynthetic stems that reproduce sexually by aerial spores. Today, whisk ferns can be found in some areas of Florida and in the tropics. Sphenophytes (**horsetails**) have green jointed stems with occasional clusters of leaves or branches. Their cell walls contain silica that give the stem a rough texture. These plants were used by pioneers to scrub dishes—thus their name, scouring rushes. In cooler regions of North America, horsetails grow as weeds along roadsides. **Ferns** are the most successful group of seedless vascular plants, occupying habitats from the desert to tropical rain forests. Most ferns are small plants that lack woody tissue. An exception is the tree ferns found in tropical regions. Many cultivated ferns are available for home gardeners.

In this lab study you will investigate the diversity of pterophytes, including whisk ferns, horsetails, and a variety of ferns. The plants on demonstration are sporophytes, the dominant generation in seedless vascular plants. You will investigate the life cycle of a fern in Lab Study C, Fern Life Cycle.

Procedure

1. Examine a living **whisk fern** (*Psilotum nudum*) on demonstration. This is one of only two extant genera of psilophytes.

2. Observe the spherical structures on the stem. If possible, cut one open and determine the function of these structures. Note the dichotomous branching, typical of the earliest land plants.

3. Examine the **horsetails** (*Equisetum* sp.) on demonstration. Note the ribs and ridges in the stem. Also examine the nodes or joints along the stem where branches and leaves may occur in some species. Locate the **strobili** in the living or preserved specimens on demonstration. These are clusters of **sporangia,** which produce **spores.**

4. Examine the living **ferns** on demonstration. Note the deeply dissected leaves, which arise from an underground stem called a **rhizome,** which functions like a root to anchor the plant. Roots arise from the rhizome. Observe the dark spots, or **sori** (sing. **sorus**), which are clusters of sporangia, on the underside of some leaves, called **sporophylls**.

Results

1. Sketch the overall structure of the whisk fern, horsetail, and fern in the margin of your lab manual. Label structures where appropriate.

2. Are there any leaves on the whisk fern? On the horsetails?

3. Are sporangia present on the whisk fern? On the horsetails? On the ferns?

Discussion

1. Are the spores in the sporangia produced by mitosis or meiosis?

2. Are the sporangia haploid or diploid? Think about which generation produces them.

3. Once dispersed, will these spores produce the gametophyte or sporophyte generation?

Lab Study C. Fern Life Cycle

Materials

living ferns
living fern gametophytes
with archegonia and
antheridia
living fern gametophytes
with young sporophytes
attached
stereoscopic microscope

compound microscope
prepared slide of fern
gametophytes with
archegonia, c.s.
colored pencils
Protoslo®
glycerol in dropping bottle

Introduction

In the previous Lab Study you examined the features of the fern sporophyte. In this lab study you will examine the fern life cycle in more detail, beginning with the diploid sporophyte.

Procedure

1. Examine the sporophyte leaf with sori (sporophyll) at your lab bench. Make a wet mount of a sorus, using a drop of glycerol, and do not add a cover slip. Examine the sporangia using a dissecting microscope. You will find the stalked **sporangia** in various stages of development. Find a sporangium still filled with **spores** and observe carefully for a few minutes, watching for movement. The sporangia will open and fling the spores into the glycerol.

2. Refer to Figure 6 as you observe the events and important structures in the life cycle of the fern. The haploid spores of ferns fall to the ground and grow into heart-shaped, **gametophyte** plants. All seedless terrestrial plants depend on an external source of water for a sperm to swim to an egg to effect fertilization and for growth of the resulting sporophyte plant. The sexual organs, which bear male and female gametes, are borne on the underside of the gametophyte. Egg cells are produced by mitosis in urnlike structures called **archegonia,** and sperm cells are produced by mitosis in globular structures called **antheridia.** Archegonia are usually found around the notch of the heart-shaped gametophyte, while antheridia occur over most of the undersurface.

3. To study whole gametophytes, make a slide of living gametophytes. View them using the stereoscopic microscope or the scanning lens on the compound microscope. Note their shape and color and the presence of **rhizoids,** rootlike multicellular structures. Locate archegonia and antheridia. Which surface will you need to examine? Sketch in the margin of your lab manual any details not included in Figure 6.

4. If you have seen antheridia on a gametophyte, remove the slide from the microscope. Gently but firmly press on the coverslip with a pencil eraser. View using the compound microscope first on intermediate and then on high power. Look for motile **sperm** swimming with a spiral motion. Each sperm has two flagella. Add a drop of Protoslo to slow down movement of sperm.

5. Observe the cross section of a fern gametophyte with archegonia. Each archegonium encloses an **egg,** which may be visible on your slide.

6. Make a wet mount of a fern gametophyte with a **young sporophyte** attached. Look for a young **leaf** and **root** on each sporophyte.

7. Share slides of living gametophytes with archegonia, antheridia and sperm, and sporophytes until everyone has observed each structure.

Results

1. Review the structures and processes observed, and then label the stages of fern sexual reproduction outlined in Figure 6.

2. Using colored pencils, circle those parts of the life cycle that are sporophytic (diploid). Use another color to encircle the gametophytic (haploid) stages of the life cycle. Highlight the processes of meiosis and mitosis.

Discussion

Refer to Figure 2, the generalized diagram of the plant life cycle, and Figure 6, a representation of the fern life cycle.

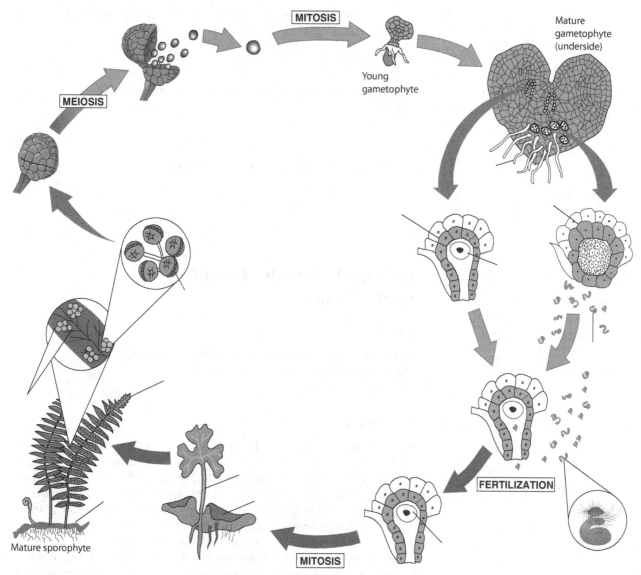

MITOSIS

MEIOSIS

Young
gametophyte

Mature
gametophyte
(underside)

FERTILIZATION

MITOSIS

Mature sporophyte

Figure 6.
Fern life cycle. The familiar leafy fern plant is the sporophyte, which alternates
with a small, heart-shaped gametophyte. Review this life cycle, a variation of
alternation of generations, and label the structures and processes described in
Lab Study C. *Using colored pencils, highlight the haploid and diploid structures in
different colors.*

1. Are the spores produced by the fern sporophyte formed by meiosis or
    mitosis?

2. Do the spores belong to the gametophyte or the sporophyte generation?

3. Are the gametes produced by mitosis or meiosis?

4. Are the archegonia and antheridia haploid or diploid? Think about which generation produces them.

5. Is the dominant generation for the fern the gametophyte or the sporophyte?

6. Can you suggest any ecological role for ferns?

Lab Study D. Fossils of Seedless Vascular Plants

Materials

fossils of extinct lycophytes (*Lepidodendron, Sigillaria*)
fossils of extinct sphenophytes (*Calamites*)
fossils of extinct ferns

Introduction

If we went back in time 300 million years to the Carboniferous period, we would encounter a wide variety of vertebrate amphibians moving about vast swamps dominated by spore-bearing forest trees. Imagine a forest of horsetails and lycophytes the size of trees, amphibians as large as alligators, and enormous dragonflies and roaches! Seedless plants were at their peak during this period and were so prolific that their carbonized remains form the bulk of Earth's coal deposits. Among the most spectacular components of the coal-swamp forest were 100-foot-tall lycophyte trees belonging to the fossil genera *Lepidodendron* and *Sigillaria,* tree ferns, and 60-foot-tall horsetails assigned to the fossil genus *Calamites* (Figures 3 and 7).

Procedure

Examine flattened fossil stems of *Lepidodendron, Sigillaria, Calamites,* and fossil fern foliage, all of which were recovered from coal mine tailings. Compare these with their living relatives, the lycophytes (club mosses), sphenophytes (horsetails), and ferns, which today are diminutive plants found in restricted habitats.

Results

1. For each phylum of seedless vascular plants, describe those characteristics that are similar for both living specimens and fossils. For example, do you observe dichotomous branching and similar shape and form of leaves, stems, or sporangia? Refer to the living specimens or your sketches.

Figure 7.
Seedless vascular plants of the Carboniferous period. (a) Reconstruction of a swamp forest dominated by lycophytes (b) *Lepidodendron* and (c) *Sigillaria*. (d) *Calamites* was a relative of horsetails. (*No. Geo. 7500c, Field Museum of Natural History, Chicago*)

Lycophytes:

Sphenophytes:

Ferns:

2. Sketch below the overall structure of the fossils. How would you recognize these fossils at a later date? Label structures where appropriate.

b, c, d: Adapted from James D. Mauseth, *Botany: An Introduction to Plant Biology*, fig. 23.3, p. 667 (Sudbury, MA: Jones and Bartlett Publishers, 1991), www.jbpub.com. Reprinted with permission.

Discussion

The lycophytes, sphenophytes, and ferns were once the giants of the plant kingdom and dominated the landscape. Explain why they are presently restricted to certain habitats and are relatively small in stature.

Questions for Review

1. Complete Table 3, indicating the ancestral and derived features of seedless vascular plants relative to success in land environments. Recall that in this context the term *ancestral* means a shared trait, while the term *derived* indicates an adaptation to land. For example, traits shared with the nonvascular plants (such as sperm requiring water for fertilization) are ancestral, while the presence of vascular tissue is derived.

Table 3
Ancestral and Derived Features of Seedless Vascular
Plants as They Relate to Adaptation to Land

Ancestral Features	Derived Features

2. For each of the listed features, describe its contribution, if any, to the success of land plants.

gametangium

cuticle

rhizoid

motile sperm

vascular tissue

gemma

3. Complete Table 4. Identify the function of the structures listed. Indicate whether they are part of the gametophyte or sporophyte generation, and provide an example of a plant that has this structure.

4. What is the major difference between the alternation of generations in the life cycles of nonvascular plants and seedless vascular plants?

Table 4

Structures and Functions of the Nonvascular Plants and Seedless Vascular Plants

Structure	Function	Sporophyte/ Gametophyte	Example
Antheridium			
Archegonium			
Spore			
Gamete			
Rhizome			
Gemma			
Sporangium			
Strobilus			
Sorus			

Applying Your Knowledge

1. The fossil record provides little information about ancient mosses. Do you think that nonvascular plants could ever have been large tree-sized plants? Provide evidence from your investigations to support your answer.

2. On a walk through a botanical garden, you notice a small leafy plant that is growing along the edge of a small stream in a shady nook. You hypothesize that this plant is a lycophyte. What information can you gather to test your hypothesis?

3. Fern antheridia release sperm that then swim toward archegonia in a watery film. The archegonia release a fluid containing chemicals that attract the sperm. This is an example of chemotaxis, the movement of cells or organisms in response to a chemical. What is the significance of chemotaxis to fern (and moss) reproduction?

4. Scientists investigating the evolutionary history (phylogeny) of land plants represent their hypotheses as phylogenetic trees or branching diagrams. Groups of plants that share a common ancestor are called clades, which are represented as lines connected at a branching point (the common ancestor). See the example below.

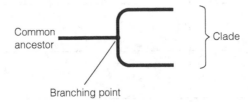

Which two of the phylogenetic trees below best represents the evolutionary history of land plants? Explain your choice of tree using your results from this laboratory topic.

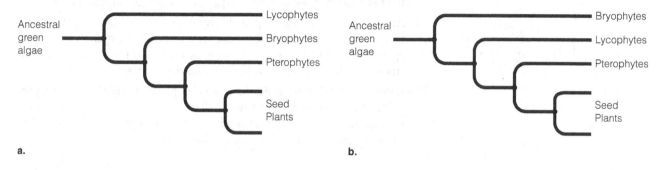

a.

b.

5. Heterospory occasionally occurs in lycophytes and ferns, and in all seed plants. Botanists are convinced that heterospory must have originated more than once in the evolution of plants. Can you suggest one or more advantages that heterospory might provide to plants?

Investigative Extensions

C-Ferns, Ceratopteris, are excellent experimental organisms for investigating the alternation of generations life cycle, comparisons of seedless vascular plants with seed plants, and the physiology of ferns. These small ferns have a short life cycle of 12 days from spore to spore, and they can be grown successfully in small laboratory spaces. Amazingly, the motile sperm, easily visible under the microscope, can swim for two hours in buffer! The following are questions that you might investigate.

1. Fern archegonia secrete phermones to attract swimming sperm for fertilization, an example of chemotaxis (see question 3 in Applying Your Knowledge). Are sperm attracted to other compounds as well, including organic acids that might be present in the fluid secreted by the archegonia? Are there other compounds that might also be attractants? What are the common characteristics of the compounds that are attractants, for example, type of compound or chemical structure?

2. *C-Ferns* produce two types of gametophytes, hermaphrodites (both archegonia and antheridia present) and males (antheridia only). What factors affect the proportion of hermaphrodite and male gametophytes in the population, for example, temperature, light, or population density?

3. Are sperm from male gametophytes more or less attracted by pheromones compared with sperm from the hermaphrodites? Do sperm from both types of gametophytes respond to the same concentration of pheromones or other organic attractants?

Resources, laboratory procedures and preparation instructions are provided at the *C-Fern* web site http://cfern.bio.utk.edu/index.html. Growing materials are available at Carolina Biological Supply, including *C-Fern* Chemotaxis Kit and *C-Fern* Culture Kit.

 ## Student Media Activities and Investigations

Activities—Ch. 29: Highlights of Plant Phylogeny; Moss Life Cycle; Fern Life Cycle
Investigations—Ch. 29: What Are the Different Stages of a Fern Life Cycle?
www.masteringbio.com

References

Berg, L. R. *Introductory Botany: Plants, People and the Environment*, 2nd ed. Belmont, CA: Thomson Brooks/Cole, 2007.

Hickock, L. G., and T. R. Warne. *C-Fern Manual*. Burlington, NC: Carolina Biological Supply, 2000.

Mauseth, J. D. *Botany: An Introduction to Plant Biology*, 3rd ed. Sudbury, MA: Jones and Bartlett Publishers, 2003.

Raven, P. H., R. F. Evert, and S. E. Eichhorn. *Biology of Plants*, 7th ed. New York: W. H. Freeman Publishers, 2004.

Websites

The Tree of Life Web Project is a collaborative project of biologists worldwide. Information is provided on all major groups of living organisms including land plants: http://tolweb.org/Embryophytes

An introduction to land plants, including morphology, evolution, and fossils. Images and resources provided: http://www.ucmp.berkeley.edu/plants/plantae.html

Fern basics (click on Learn More about Ferns), images and current research: http://amerfernsoc.org/

Links to images of plants: http://botit.botany.wisc.edu/images/130/

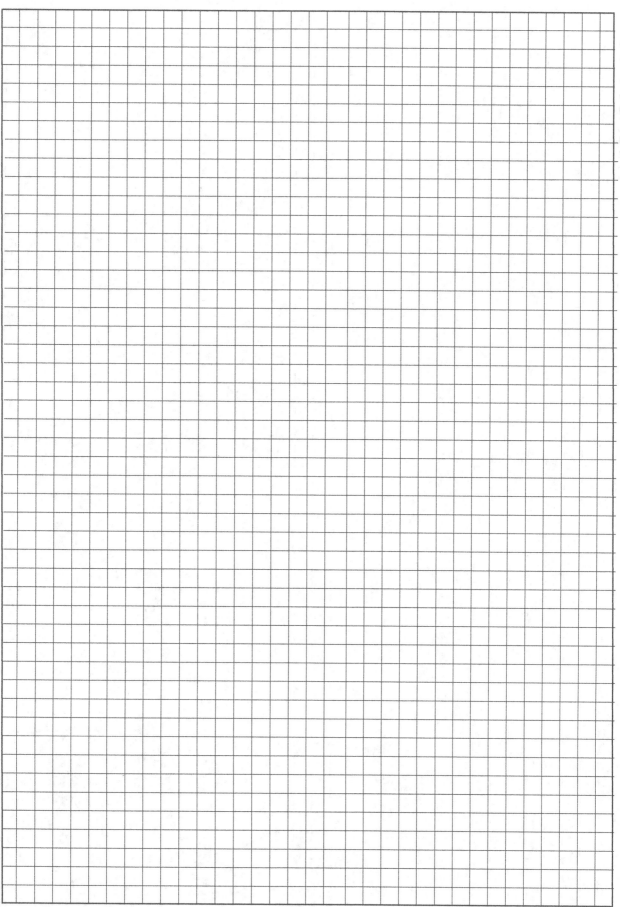

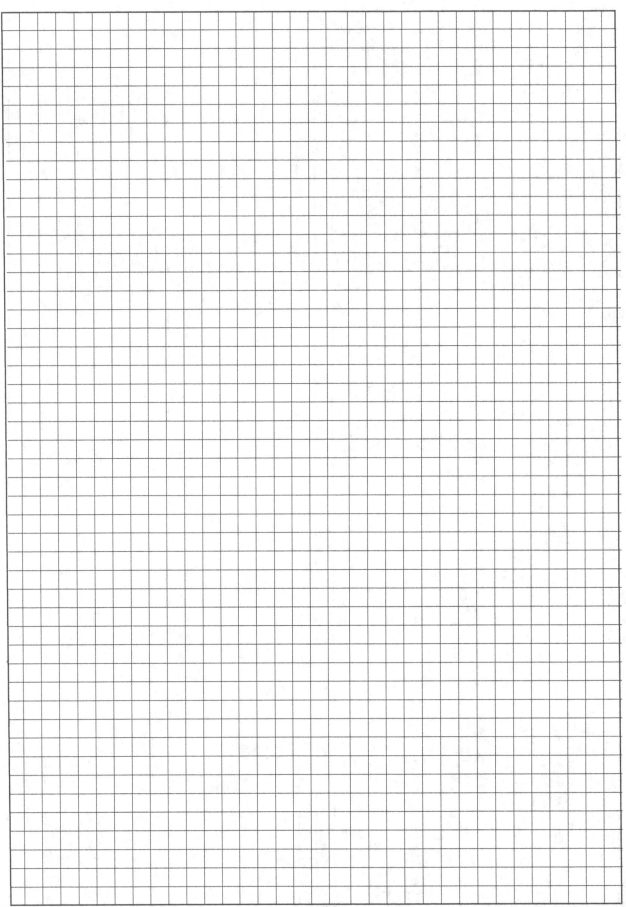

Plant Diversity: Seed Plants

 Before lab, read the following material on gymnosperms and angiosperms and complete Table 1 by listing (and comparing) the traits of each.

Laboratory Objectives

After completing this lab topic, you should be able to:

1. Identify examples of the phyla of seed plants.
2. Describe the life cycle of a gymnosperm (pine tree) and an angiosperm.
3. Describe features of flowers that ensure pollination by insects, birds, bats, and wind.
4. Describe factors influencing pollen germination.
5. Identify types of fruits, recognize examples, and describe dispersal mechanisms.
6. Relate the structures of seed plants to their functions in the land environment.
7. Compare the significant features of life cycles for various land plants and state their evolutionary importance.
8. Summarize major trends in the evolution of land plants and provide evidence from your laboratory investigations.

Gymnosperms

For over 500 million years, plants have been adapting to the rigors of the land environment. The nonvascular bryophytes with their small and simple bodies survived in moist habitats, habitats moist at least for part of their life cycle. During the cool Carboniferous period, vascular seedless plants dominated the landscape of the swamp forests that covered much of the earth. Although these plants were more complex and better adapted to the challenges of the land environment, they still were dependent on water for sperm to swim to the egg. During the Mesozoic era, 150 million years ago, Earth became warmer and drier and the swamp forests declined, presenting another challenge to terrestrial plants and animals. Earth at that time was a world dominated by reptilian vertebrates, including the flying,

From *Investigating Biology Laboratory Manual,* Sixth Edition, Judith G. Morgan and M. Eloise Brown Carter. Copyright © 2008 by Pearson Education, Inc. Published by Benjamin Cummings, Inc. All rights reserved.

running, and climbing dinosaurs. The landscape was dominated by a great variety of seed-bearing plants called **gymnosperms** (literally, "naked seeds"), which in the Carboniferous period had been restricted to dry sites. During the Mesozoic, a number of distinct gymnosperm groups diversified, and a few of the spore-bearing plants survived.

Vertebrate animals became fully terrestrial during the Mesozoic with the emergence of reptiles, which were free from a dependence on water for sexual reproduction and development. The development of the amniotic egg along with an internal method of fertilization made this major transition possible. The amniotic egg carries its own water supply and nutrients, permitting early embryonic development to occur on dry land, a great distance from external water. In an analogous manner, the gymnosperms became free from dependence on water through the development of a process of internal fertilization via the pollen grain and development of a seed, which contains a dormant embryo with a protective cover and special nutrient tissue.

Several features of the gymnosperms have been responsible for their success. They have reduced (smaller-sized) gametophytes; the male gametophyte is a multinucleated pollen grain, and the female gametophyte is small and retained within the sporangium in the ovule of the sporophyte generation. The pollen grain is desiccation resistant and adapted for wind pollination, removing the necessity for fertilization in a watery medium. The pollen tube conveys the sperm nucleus to an egg cell, and the embryonic sporophyte develops within the gametophyte tissues, which are protected by the previous sporophyte generation. The resulting seed is not only protected from environmental extremes, but also is packed with nutritive materials and can be dispersed away from the parent plant. In addition, gymnosperms have advanced vascular tissues: xylem for transporting water and nutrients and phloem for transporting photosynthetic products. The xylem cells are called *tracheids* and are more efficient for transport than those of the seedless vascular plants.

Angiosperms

A visit to Earth 60 million years ago, during the late Cretaceous period, would reveal a great diversity of mammals and birds and a landscape dominated by **flowering plants**, or **angiosperms** (phylum **Anthophyta**). Ultimately, these plants would diversify and become the most numerous, widespread, and important plants on Earth. Angiosperms now occupy well over 90% of the vegetated surface of Earth and contribute virtually 100% of our agricultural food plants.

The evolution of the flower resulted in enormous advances in the efficient transfer and reception of pollen. Whereas gymnosperms are all wind-pollinated, producing enormous amounts of pollen that reach the appropriate species by chance, the process of flower pollination is mediated by specific agents—insects, birds, and bats—in addition to water and wind. Pollination agents such as the insect are attracted to the flower with its rewards of nectar and pollen. Animal movements provide precise placement of pollen on the receptive portion of the female structures, increasing the probability of fertilization. The process also enhances the opportunity for cross-fertilization among distant plants and therefore the possibility of increased genetic variation.

Angiosperm reproduction follows the trend for reduction in the size of the gametophyte. The pollen grain is the male gametophyte, and the eight-nucleated **embryo sac** is all that remains of the female gametophyte. This generation continues to be protected and dependent on the adult sporophyte plant. The female gametophyte provides nutrients for the developing sporophyte embryo through a unique triploid **endosperm** tissue. Another unique feature of angiosperms is the **fruit.** The seeds of the angiosperm develop within the flower ovary, which matures into the fruit. This structure provides protection and enhances dispersal of the young sporophyte into new habitats.

In addition to advances in reproductive biology, the angiosperms evolved other advantageous traits. All gymnosperms are trees or shrubs, with a large investment in woody, persistent tissue; and their life cycles are long (5 or more years before they begin to reproduce and 2 to 3 years to produce a seed). Flowering plants, on the other hand, can be woody, but many are herbaceous, with soft tissues that survive from one to a few years. It is possible for angiosperms to go from seed to seed in less than one year. As you perform the exercises in this lab, think about the significance of this fact in terms of the evolution of this group. How might generation length affect the rate of evolution? Angiosperms also have superior conducting tissues. Xylem tissue is composed of *tracheids* (as in gymnosperms), but also contains large-diameter, open-ended *vessels*. The phloem cells, called *sieve-tube members,* provide more efficient transport of the products of photosynthesis.

Review the characteristics of gymnosperms and angiosperms described in this introduction, and summarize in Table 1 the advantages of these groups relative to their success on land. You should be able to list several characteristics for each. At the end of the lab, you will be asked to modify and complete the table, based on your investigations.

You will want to return to this table after the laboratory to be sure that the table is complete and that you are familiar with all these important features.

EXERCISE 1

Gymnosperms

The term *gymnosperms* refers to a diverse group of seed plants that do not produce flowers. Although they share many characteristics, including the production of pollen, they represent four distinct groups, or phyla. In this exercise, you will observe members of these phyla and investigate the life cycle of a pine, one of the most common gymnosperms.

Table 1
Traits for Gymnosperms and Angiosperms
Relative to Their Success on Land

	Adaptation to the Land Environment
Gymnosperms	
Angiosperms	

Lab Study A. Phyla of Gymnosperms

Materials

living or pressed examples of conifers, ginkgos, cycads, and Mormon tea

Introduction

Gymnosperms are composed of several phyla. The largest and best known is Coniferophyta, which includes pines and other cone-bearing trees and shrubs. Cycads (Cycadophyta), which have a palmlike appearance, are found primarily in tropical regions scattered around the world. Ginkgos (Ginkgophyta), with their flat fan-shaped leaves, are native to Asia and are prized as urban trees. An extract of Ginkgo is used as an herbal medicine purported to improve memory. Gnetophyta is composed of three distinct and unusual groups of plants: gnetums, which are primarily vines of Asia, Africa, and South America; *Welwitschia*, a rare desert plant with two leathery leaves; and Mormon tea (*Ephedra*), desert shrubs of North and Central America. Compounds from *Ephedra*, ephedrines, used in diet aids and decongestants, have raised serious concerns due to side effects including cardiac arrest.

Procedure

1. Observe demonstration examples of all phyla of gymnosperms and be able to recognize their representatives. Note any significant ecological and economic role for these plants.

2. Record your observations in Table 2.

Table 2
Phyla of Gymnosperms

Phyla	Examples	Characteristics/Comments
Coniferophyta		
Ginkgophyta		
Cycadophyta		
Gnetophyta		

Results

1. In the margin of your manual, sketch the overall structure of the plants. Label structures where appropriate.

2. Are there any reproductive structures present for these plants? If so, make notes in the margin of your lab manual.

Discussion

1. What are the key characteristics shared by all gymnosperms?

2. What is the ecological role of conifers in forest systems?

3. What economically important products are provided by conifers?

Lab Study B. Pine Life Cycle

Materials

living or preserved pine branch,
   male and female cones
   (1, 2, and 3 years old)
fresh or dried pine pollen or
   prepared slide of pine pollen

coverslips
prepared slides of male and female
   pine cones
colored pencils
slides

 Review the pine life cycle (Figure 1) before you begin. Follow along as you complete the exercise.

Introduction

All gymnosperms are **wind-pollinated** trees or shrubs, most bearing unisexual, male, and female reproductive structures on different parts of the same plant. Gymnosperms are **heterosporous**, producing two kinds of spores: male **microspores**, which develop into **pollen**, and female **megaspores.** The megaspore develops into the female gametophyte, which is not free-living as with ferns but retained within the **megasporangium** and nourished by the sporophyte parent plant. Numerous pollen grains (the male gametophytes) are produced in each **microsporangium**, and when they are mature they are released into the air and conveyed by wind currents to the female cone. **Pollen tubes** grow through the tissue of the megasporangium, and the **sperm nucleus** is released to fertilize the egg. After fertilization, development results in the formation of an **embryo.** A **seed** is a dormant embryo embedded in nutrient tissue of the female gametophyte and surrounded by the hardened sporangium wall, or **seed coat.**

 Having trouble with life cycles? The key to success is to determine where meiosis occurs and to remember the ploidal level for the gametophyte and sporophyte.

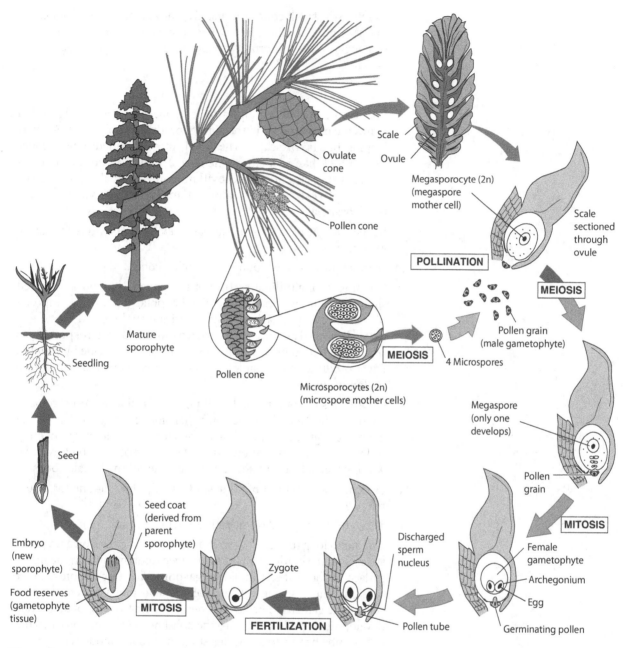

Figure 1.
Pine life cycle. Observe the structures and processes as described in Exercise 1.
Using colored pencils, indicate the structures that are haploid or diploid. Circle the
terms mitosis, meiosis, *and* fertilization.

Procedure

1. Pine sporophyte.

   a. Examine the pine branch and notice the arrangement of leaves in a
      bundle. A new twig at the end of the branch is in the process of pro-
      ducing new clusters of leaves. Is this plant haploid or diploid?

105

   b. Examine the small **cones** produced at the end of the pine branch on this specimen or others in lab. Recall that cones contain clusters of sporangia. What important process occurs in the sporangia?

   c. Locate an ovulate cone and a pollen cone. Elongated male **pollen cones** are present only in the spring, producing pollen within overlapping bracts, or scales. The small, more rounded female cones (which look like miniature pine cones) are produced on stem tips in the spring and are called **ovulate cones.** Female cones persist for several years. Observe the overlapping scales, which contain the sporangia.

   d. In the margin of your lab manual, sketch observations for future reference.

2. Male gametophyte—development in pollen cones.

   a. Examine a longitudinal section of the pollen cone on a prepared slide and identify its parts. Observe that pollen cones are composed of radiating scales, each of which carries two elongated sacs on its lower surface. The sacs are the **microsporangia. Microsporocytes** (microspore mother cells) within microsporangia divide by meiosis. Each produces four haploid **microspores,** which develop into **pollen grains.**

   b. Observe a slide of pine pollen. If pollen is available, you can make a wet mount. Note the wings on either side of the grain. The pollen grain is the greatly reduced male gametophyte. The outer covering of the pollen is desiccation resistant. Once mature, pollen will be wind dispersed, sifting down into the scales of the female cones.

   c. Sketch, in the margin of your lab manual, observations for future reference.

3. Female gametophyte—development in ovulate cones.

   a. Examine a longitudinal section of a young ovulate cone on a prepared slide. Note the **ovule** (containing the megasporangium) on the upper surface of the scales. Diploid **megasporocytes** (megaspore mother cells) contained inside will produce haploid **megaspores,** the first cells of the gametophyte generation. In the first year of ovulate cone development, pollen sifts into the soft bracts (pollination) and the pollen tube begins to grow, digesting the tissues of the ovule.

   b. Observe a second-year cone at your lab bench. During the second year, the ovule develops a multicellular female gametophyte with two archegonia in which an egg will form. Fertilization will not occur until the second year, when the pollen tube releases a sperm nucleus into the archegonium, where it unites with the egg to form the **zygote.** In each ovule only one of the archegonia and its zygote develops into a seed.

   c. Observe a mature cone at your lab bench. The development of the embryo sporophyte usually takes another year. The female gametophyte will provide nutritive materials stored in the seed for the early stages of growth. The outer tissues of the ovule will harden to form the **seed coat.**

   d. In the margin of your lab manual, sketch observations for future reference.

Results

1. Review the structures and processes observed.
2. Using colored pencils, indicate the structures of the pine life cycle in Figure 1 that are haploid or diploid, and circle the processes of mitosis, meiosis, and fertilization.

Discussion

1. What is the function of the wings on the pollen grain?

2. Why is wind-dispersed pollen an important phenomenon in the evolution of plants?

3. Are microspores and megaspores produced by mitosis or meiosis?

4. Can you think of at least two ways in which pine seeds are dispersed?

5. One of the major trends in plant evolution is the reduction in size of the gametophytes. Describe the male and female gametophyte in terms of size and location.

EXERCISE 2
Angiosperms

All flowering plants (angiosperms) are classified in the phylum **Anthophyta** (Gk. *anthos,* "flower"). A unique characteristic of angiosperms is the **carpel,** a vessel in which ovules are enclosed. After fertilization, the ovule develops into a seed (as in the gymnosperms), while the carpel matures into a fruit (unique to angiosperms). Other important aspects of angiosperm reproduction include additional reduction of the gametophyte, double fertilization, and an increase in the rapidity of the reproduction process.

The **flowers** of angiosperms are composed of male and female reproductive structures, which are frequently surrounded by attractive or protective leaflike structures collectively known as the **perianth**. The flower functions both to protect the developing gametes and to ensure pollination and fertilization. Although many angiosperm plants are self- fertile, cross-fertilization is important in maintaining genetic diversity. Plants, rooted and stationary, often require transfer agents to complete fertilization. A variety of insects, birds, and mammals transfer pollen from flower to flower. The pollen then germinates into a pollen tube and grows through the female carpel to deliver the sperm to the egg.

Plants must attract pollinators to the flower. What are some features of flowers that attract pollinators? Color and scent are important, as is the shape of the flower. Nectar and pollen provide nutritive rewards for the pollinators as well. The shape and form of some of the flowers are structured to accommodate pollinators of specific size and structure, providing landing platforms, guidelines, and even special mechanisms for the placement of pollen on body parts. While the flower is encouraging the visitation by one type of pollinator, it also may be excluding visitation by others. The more specific the relationship between flower and pollinator, the more probable that the pollen of that species will be successfully transferred. But many successful flowers have no specific adaptations for particular pollinators and are visited by a wide variety of pollinators.

Some plants do not have colorful, showy flowers and are rather inconspicuous, often dull in color, and lacking a perianth. These plants are usually wind-pollinated, producing enormous quantities of pollen and adapted to catch pollen in the wind.

The origin and diversification of angiosperms cannot be understood apart from the coevolutionary role of animals in the reproductive process. Colorful petals, strong scents, nectars, food bodies, and unusual perianth shapes all relate to pollinator visitation. Major trends in the evolution of angiosperms involve the development of mechanisms to exploit a wide variety of pollinators.

In Lab Study A, you will investigate a variety of flowers, observing their shape, structure, and traits that might attract pollinators of various kinds. Following this, in Lab Study B, you will use a key to identify the probable pollinators for some of these flowers. You will follow the life cycle of the lily in Lab Study C and complete the lab by using another key to identify types of fruits and their dispersal mechanisms.

Lab Study A. Flower Morphology

Materials

living flowers provided by the instructor and/or students
stereoscopic microscope

Introduction

Working in teams of two students, you will investigate the structure of the flower (Figure 2). The instructor will provide a variety of flowers, and you may have brought some with you to lab. You will need to take apart each flower carefully to determine its structure, since it is unlikely that all your flowers will follow the simple diagram used to illustrate the structures. Your observations will be the basis for predicting probable pollinators in Lab Study B.

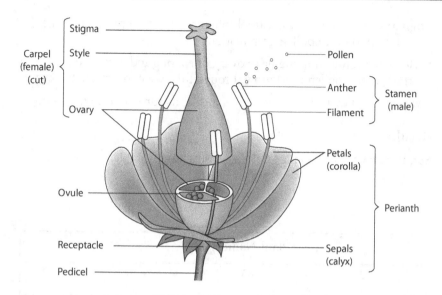

Figure 2.

Flower structures. Determine the structures of flowers in the laboratory by reviewing this general diagram.

Procedure

1. Examine fresh flowers of four different species, preferably with different floral characteristics.

2. Identify the parts of each flower using Figure 2 and the list provided following the heading Floral Parts. You may be able to determine the floral traits for large, open flowers by simply observing. However, most flowers will require that you remove the floral structures from the outside toward the center of the flower. Some flowers or structures may require the use of the stereoscopic microscope. For example, the ovary is positively identified by the presence of tiny crystal-like ovules, and these are best seen with the stereoscopic scope.

3. In the margin of your lab manual, sketch any flower shapes or structures that you might need to refer to in the future.

4. Record the results of your observations in Table 3. You will determine pollinators in Lab Study B.

Floral Parts

Pedicel: stalk that supports the flower.

Receptacle: tip of the pedicel where the flower parts attach.

Sepal: outer whorl of bracts, which may be green, brown, or colored like the petals; may appear as small scales or be petal-like.

Calyx: all the sepals, collectively.

Petal: colored, white, or even greenish whorl of bracts located just inside the sepals.

Corolla: all the petals, collectively.

Stamen: pollen-bearing structure, composed of filament and anther.

Filament: thin stalk that supports the anther.

Anther: pollen-producing structure.

Carpel: female reproductive structure, composed of the stigma, style, and ovary, often pear-shaped and located in the center of the flower.

Stigma: receptive tip of the carpel, often sticky or hairy, where pollen is placed; important to pollen germination.

Style: tissue connecting stigma to ovary, often long and narrow, but may be short or absent; pollen must grow through this tissue to fertilize the egg.

Ovary: base of carpel; protects ovules inside, matures to form the fruit.

Results

Summarize your observations of flower structure in Table 3.

Table 3
Flower Morphology and Pollinators

Features	Plant Names			
	1	2	3	4
Number of petals				
Number of sepals				
Parts absent (petals, stamens, etc.)				
Color				
Scent (+/-)				
Nectar (+/-)				
Shape (including corolla shape: tubular, star, etc.)				
Special features (landing platform, guidelines, nectar spur, etc.)				
Predicted pollinator (see Lab Study B)				

Discussion

What structures or characteristics did you observe in your (or other teams') investigations that you predict are important to pollination?

 Student Media Videos—Ch.30: Flower Blooming (Time Lapse); Flowering Plant Life Cycle

---

Lab Study B. Pollinators

Materials

living flowers provided by the instructor and/or students
stereoscopic microscope

Introduction

Flowers with inconspicuous sepals and petals are usually pollinated by wind. Most showy flowers are pollinated by animals. Some pollinators tend to be attracted to particular floral traits, and, in turn, some groups of plants have coevolved with a particular pollination agent that ensures successful reproduction. Other flowers are generalists, pollinated by a variety of organisms, and still others may be visited by only one specific pollinator. Based on the floral traits that attract common pollinators (bees, flies, butterflies, and hummingbirds), you will predict the probable pollinator for some of your flowers using a dichotomous key. (Remember, *dichotomous* refers to the branching pattern and means "divided into two parts.")

In biology, we use a key to systematically separate groups of organisms based on sets of characteristics. Most keys are based on couplets, or pairs of characteristics, from which you must choose one or the other, thus, the term *dichotomous*. For example, the first choice of characteristics in a couplet might be *plants with showy flowers and a scent,* and the other choice in the pair might be *plants with tiny, inconspicuous flowers with no scent.* You must choose one or the other statement. In the next step, you would choose from a second pair of statements listed directly below your first choice. With each choice, you would narrow the group more and more until, as in this case, the pollinator is identified. *Each couplet or pair of statements from which you must choose will be identified by the same letter or number.*

Key to Pollination

I. Sepals and petals reduced or inconspicuous; feathery or relatively large stigma; flower with no odor **wind**

II. Sepals and/or petals large, easily identified; stigma not feathery; flower with or without odor

    A. Sepals and petals white or subdued (greenish or burgundy); distinct odor

        1. Odor strong, heavy, sweet **moth**

        2. Odor strong, fermenting or fruitlike; flower parts and pedicel strong **bat**

        3. Odor of sweat, feces, or decaying meat **fly**

    B. Sepals and/or petals colored; odor may or may not be present

        1. Flower shape regular or irregular,* but not tubular

            a. Flower shape irregular; sepals or petals blue, yellow, or orange; petal adapted to serve as a "landing platform"; may have dark lines on petals; sweet, fragrant odor **bee**

            b. Flower shape regular; odor often fruity, spicy, sweet, or carrionlike **beetle**

        2. Flower shape tubular

            a. Strong, sweet odor **butterfly**

            b. Little or no odor; flower usually red **hummingbird**

*A regular flower shape is one that has radial symmetry (like a daisy or carnation), with similar parts (such as petals) having similar size and shape. Irregular flowers have bilateral symmetry.

Procedure

Using the key above, classify the flowers used in Lab Study A based on their floral traits and method of pollination.

Results

1. Record your results in Table 3.
2. If you made sketches of any of your flowers, you may want to indicate the pollinator associated with that flower.

Discussion

1. Review the Key to Pollination and describe the characteristics of flowers that are adapted for pollination by each of the following agents:

    a. wind

    b. hummingbird

    c. bat

2. Discuss with your lab partner other ways in which keys are used in biology. Record your answers in the space provided.

Student Media Videos—Ch.30: Bee Pollinating; Bat Pollinating Agave Plant

Lab Study C. Angiosperm Life Cycle

Materials

pollen tube growth medium in dropper bottles
dropper bottle of water
petri dish with filter paper to fit inside
prepared slides of lily anthers and ovary

dissecting probe
brush bristles
compound microscope
flowers for pollen

Introduction

In this lab study, you will study the life cycle of flowering plants, including the formation of pollen, pollination, fertilization of the egg, and formation of the seed and fruit. You will also investigate the germination of the pollen grain as it grows toward the egg cell.

Refer to Figures 2 (flower structures) and 3 (angiosperm life cycle) as you complete the exercise.

Procedure

1. Pollen grain—the male gametophyte.
   a. Examine a prepared slide of a cross section through the **stamens** of *Lilium.* The slide shows six anthers and may include a centrally located ovary that contains ovules.
   b. Observe a single **anther,** which is composed of four **anther sacs** (microsporangia). Note the formation of **microspores** (with a single nucleus) from diploid **microsporocytes** (microspore mother cells). You may also see mature **pollen grains** with two nuclei.

2. Development of the female gametophyte.
   a. Examine a prepared slide of the *Lilium* ovary and locate the developing ovules. Each **ovule,** composed of the megasporangium and other tissues, contains a diploid **megasporocyte** (megaspore mother cell), which produces **megaspores** (haploid), only one of which survives. The megaspore will divide three times by mitosis to produce the eight nuclei in the **embryo sac,** which is the greatly reduced female gametophyte. Note that angiosperms do not even produce an archegonium.

113

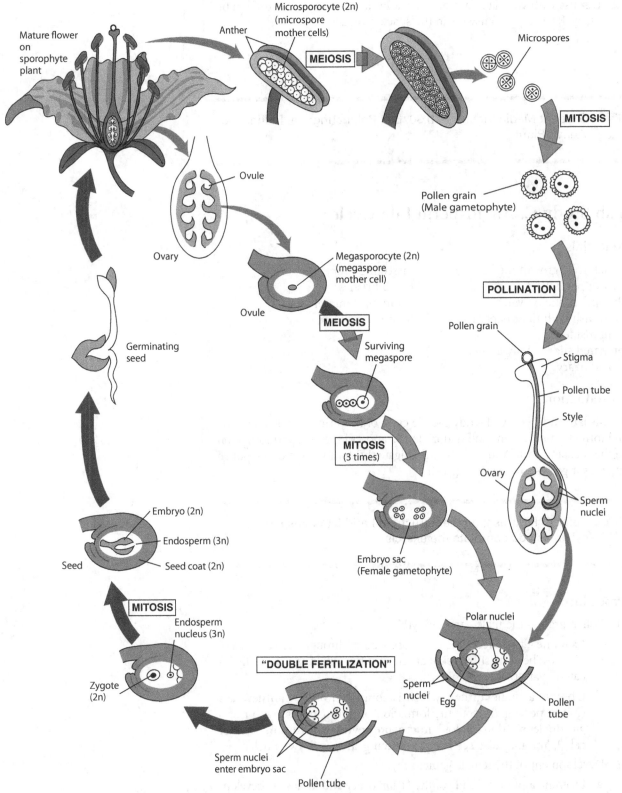

Adapted from N. Campbell, J. Reece, and L. Mitchell, *Biology*, 5th ed. (Menlo Park, CA: Benjamin/Cummings, 1999), © 1999 The Benjamin/Cummings Publishing Company.

Figure 3.
Angiosperm life cycle. Observe the structures and processes as described in Exercise 2. *Using colored pencils, indicate the structures that are haploid or diploid. Circle the terms* mitosis, meiosis, *and* double fertilization.

b. Your slide will not contain all stages of development, and it is almost impossible to find a section that includes all eight nuclei. Locate the three nuclei near the opening to the ovule. One of these is called the **egg cell.** The two nuclei in the center are the **polar nuclei** (or central cell).

3. Pollination and fertilization.

When pollen grains are mature, the anthers split and the pollen is released. When pollen reaches the stigma, it germinates to produce a **pollen tube,** which grows down the style and eventually comes into contact with the opening to the ovule. During this growth, one pollen nucleus divides into two **sperm nuclei.** One sperm nucleus fuses with the egg to form the **zygote,** and the second fuses with the two polar nuclei to form the triploid **endosperm,** which will develop into a rich nutritive material for the support and development of the embryo. The fusion of the two sperm nuclei with nuclei of the embryo sac is referred to as **double fertilization.** Formation of triploid endosperm and double fertilization are unique to angiosperms.

Once the pollen grain is deposited on the stigma of the flower, it must grow through the stylar tissue to reach the ovule. You will examine pollen tube growth by placing pollen in pollen growth medium to stimulate germination. Pollen from some plants germinates easily; for others a very specific chemical environment is required. Work with a partner, following the next steps.

a. Using a dissecting probe, transfer some pollen from the anthers of one of the plants available in the lab to a slide on which there are 2 to 3 drops of pollen tube growth medium and a few brush bristles or grains of sand (to avoid crushing the pollen). Add a coverslip. Alternatively, touch an anther to the drop of medium, then add brush bristles and a coverslip.

b. Examine the pollen under the compound microscope. Observe the shape and surface features of the pollen.

c. Prepare a humidity chamber by placing moistened filter paper in a petri dish. Place the slide in the petri dish, and place it in a warm environment.

d. Examine the pollen after 30 minutes and again after 60 minutes to observe pollen tube growth. The pollen tubes should appear as long, thin tubes extending from the surface or pores in the pollen grain.

e. Record your results in Table 4 in the Results section. Indicate the plant name and the times when pollen tube germination was observed.

4. Seed and fruit development.

The zygote formed at fertilization undergoes rapid mitotic phyla, forming the embryo. The endosperm also divides; the mature ovule forms a seed. At the same time, the surrounding ovary and other floral tissues are forming the fruit. In Lab Study D, you will investigate the types of fruits and their function in dispersal.

Results

1. Review the structures and processes observed in the angiosperm life cycle, Figure 3. Indicate the haploid and diploid structures in the life cycle, using two different colored pencils.

Having trouble with life cycles? The key to success is to determine where meiosis occurs and to remember the ploidal level for the gametophyte and sporophyte.

2. Sketch observations of slides in the margin of your lab manual for later reference.

3. Record the results of pollen germination studies in Table 4. Compare your results with those of other teams who used different plants. This is particularly important if your pollen did not germinate.

Table 4
Results of Pollen Germination Studies

Plant Name	30 min(+/-)	60 min(+/-)

Discussion

1. What part of the life cycle is represented by the mature pollen grain?

2. How does the female gametophyte in angiosperms differ from the female gametophyte in gymnosperms?

3. Do you think that all pollen germinates indiscriminately on all stigmas? How might pollen germination and growth be controlled?

Lab Study D. Fruits and Dispersal

Materials

variety of fruits provided by the instructor and/or students

Introduction

The seed develops from the ovule, and inside is the embryo and its nutritive tissues. The fruit develops from the ovary or from other tissues in the flower. It provides protection for the seeds, and both the seed and the fruit may be involved in dispersal of the sporophyte embryo.

Procedure

1. Examine the fruits and seeds on demonstration.
2. Use the Key to Fruits on the next page to help you complete Table 5. Remember to include the dispersal mechanisms for fruits and their seeds in the table.

Results

1. Record in Table 5 the fruit type for each of the fruits keyed. Share results with other teams so that you have information for all fruits in the lab.

Table 5
Fruit Types and Dispersal Mechanisms

Plant Name	Fruit Type	Dispersal Method

2. For each fruit, indicate the probable method of dispersal—for example, wind, water, gravity, ingestion by birds, mammals, or insects, or adhesion to fur and socks.
3. For some fruits, the seeds rather than the fruit are adapted for dispersal. In the milkweed, for example, the winged seeds are contained in a dry ovary. Indicate in Table 5 if the seeds have structures to enhance dispersal. Recall that seeds are inside fruits. The dandelion "seed" is really a fruit with a fused ovary and seed coat.

Achene

Nut

Capsule

Legume

Follicle

Drupe

Berry

Pome

Aggregate fruit

Multiple fruit

Key to Fruits

I. Simple fruits (one ovary)
   A. Dry fruits (at maturity)
      1. Fruits with one seed
         a. Ovary wall and seed coat are fused   **achene***
         b. Ovary wall hard or woody but can be separated from the seed   **nut**
      2. Fruits with two to many seeds
         a. Ovary with several cavities (seen when cut in cross section) and several too many seeds   **capsule**
         b. Ovary with one cavity
         c. Mature ovary opens along both sides   **legume**
         d. Mature ovary opens along one side   **follicle**
   B. Fleshy fruits
      1. Ovary with one seed, which is surrounded by a very hard stone (outer covering of the seed is formed from the inner ovary wall)   **drupe**
      2. Ovary with many seeds; does not have a "stone"
         a. All of mature ovary tissue is soft and fleshy; surrounding flower tissue does not develop into fruit   **berry†**
         b. Fleshy fruit develops in part from surrounding tissue of the flower (base of sepals and petals); therefore, ovary wall seen as "core" around seeds   **pome**
II. Compound fruits (more than one ovary)
   A. Fruit formed from ovaries of many flowers   **multiple fruit**
   B. Fruit formed from several ovaries in one flower   **aggregate fruit**

*In the grass family, an achene is called a **grain**.
†Berries of some families have special names: citrus family = **hesperidium**; squash family = **pepo**.

Discussion

1. How might dry fruits be dispersed? Fleshy fruits?

2. Describe the characteristics of an achene, drupe, and berry.

Questions for Review

1. Complete Table 6. Compare mosses, ferns, conifers, and flowering plants relative to sexual life cycles and adaptations to the land environment. Return to Table 1 and modify your entries.

2. Identify the function of each of the following structures found in seed plants. Consider their function in the land environment.

   pollen grain:

   microsporangium:

   flower:

   carpel:

Table 6
Comparison of Important Characteristics of Land Plants

Features	Moss	Fern	Conifer	Flowering Plant
Gametophyte or sporophyte dominant				
Water required for fertilization				
Vascular tissue (+/–)				
Homosporous or heterosporous				
Seed (+/–)				
Pollen grain (+/–)				
Fruit (+/–)				
Examples				

seed:

fruit:

endosperm:

3. Plants have evolved a number of characteristics that attract animals and ensure pollination, but what are the benefits to animals in this relationship?

4. Why is internal fertilization essential for true terrestrial living?

Applying Your Knowledge

1. Explain how the rise in prominence of one major group (angiosperms, for example) does not necessarily result in the total replacement of a previously dominant group (gymnosperms, for example).

2. In 1994 naturalists in Australia discovered a new genus and species of conifer, *Wollemia nobilis*, growing in a remote area not far from the city of Sydney. This was the first new conifer discovered since 1948. Wollemi pine (not really a pine) is in a family that had a global distribution 90 million years ago in the Cretaceous period. Scientists used a variety of different evidence to decide where this rare tree should be placed in the "Tree of Life." What evidence would be necessary to determine that this is in the phylum Coniferophyta?

To support the conservation of this ecosystem and three groups of trees (less than 100 individuals), botanical gardens are propagating these trees for sale. Although seeds have been collected, the commercially available plants are from cuttings and tissue culture. Based on your understanding of the life cycle of conifers, why is it not practical to reproduce Wollemi pines from seed or even to sell the seeds?

3. Your neighbor's rose garden is being attacked by Japanese beetles, so she dusts her roses with an insecticide. Now, to her dismay, she realizes that the beans and squash plants in her vegetable garden are flowering, but are no longer producing vegetables. She knows beetles feed on leaves of roses and squash plants. What is the problem? Explain to your neighbor the relationship among flowers, fruits (vegetables, in the gardening language), and insects.

4. Seed plants provide food, medicine, fibers, beverages, building materials, dyes, and psychoactive drugs. Using web resources, your textbook, and library references, describe examples of human uses of plants in Table 7. Indicate whether your example is a gymnosperm or angiosperm. Based on your research, what is the relative economic importance of angiosperms and gymnosperms?

Table 7

Uses of Seed Plants: Angiosperms and Gymnosperms

Uses of Plants	Example	Angiosperm/ Gymnosperm
Food		
Beverage		
Medicine		
Fibers		
Materials		
Dyes		
Drugs		

5. Describe the major trends in the evolution of land plants.

Investigative Extensions

Pollen germinates easily in the laboratory for some species and not at all for others. In some species, a biochemical signal is required from the stigma to initiate germination. Think about the advantages to the species if pollen germinates easily or if it requires a biochemical signal. You can investigate the factors that affect pollen germination and pollen tube growth using flowers available in the laboratory that did not germinate using a general growth medium. Develop an investigation based on questions generated by your observations in this lab topic or consider one of the following suggestions.

1. Are factors present in the stigma necessary for pollen germination? Mince a small piece of the stigma in sucrose and then add it to a slide with pollen in pollen growth medium. (The sucrose concentration in the growth medium can also be varied, since this may affect pollen germination). Compare pollen germination using the stigma material from closely related species and then from those distantly related. For example, try different species of the Mustard Family or even different varieties of one species of *Brassica*. Remember that Fast Plants (*B. rapa*) are mustards as is *Arabadopsis*, another plant used in genetic studies.

2. What essential micronutrients are needed for pollen germination? Some species are sensitive to micronutrients in the growth medium, including boron and calcium. Research various growth media and test these with flowers that failed to germinate. Which of the micronutrients in the growth medium is necessary for pollen germination in your plants? Prepare growth medium omitting one of each of the components and observe pollen germination.

3. How do environmental factors, such as temperature and light, affect the rate of pollen tube growth?

Student Media Activities and Investigations

Activities—Ch.29: Terrestrial Adaptations of Plants; Highlights of Plant Phylogeny; Ch.30: Pine Life Cycle; Angiosperm Life Cycle; Ch.38: Seed and Fruit Development

Investigations—Ch.30: How Are Trees Identified by Their Leaves? Ch.38: What Tells Desert Seeds When to Germinate?

www.masteringbio.com

References

Berg, L. R. *Introductory Botany: Plants, People and the Environment*, 2nd ed. Belmont, CA: Thomson Brooks/Cole, 2007.

Levetin, E. and K. McMahon. *Plants and Society*, 4th ed. New York: McGraw Hill Co., 2006.

Mauseth, J. D. *Botany: An Introduction to Plant Biology*, 3rd ed. Sudbury, MA: Jones and Bartlett Publishers, 2003.

McLoughlin, S. and V. Vajda. "Ancient Wollemi Pines Resurgent." *American Scientist*, 2005. Vol. 93, pp. 540–547.

Raven, P. H., R. F. Evert, and S. E. Eichhorn. *Biology of Plants*, 7th ed. New York: W. H. Freeman Publishers, 2004.

Rui, M. *The Pollen Tube: A Cellular and Molecular Perspective*, New York: Springer, 2006.

Websites

Interesting and informative sites describing human uses of plants. *Wayne's Word: A Newsletter of Natural History Trivia:*
http://daphne.palomar.edu/wayne/wayne.htm

Tree of Life Project includes phylogeny of living organisms, movies, references, current research, and ideas for independent investigations:
http://tolweb.org/tree?group=Spermatopsida&contgroup=Embryophytes

University of California Berkeley Museum of Palentology site with images and resources for both living and fossil seed plants:
http://www.ucmp.berkeley.edu/plants/plantae.html

Images, maps and additional links for plants of North America:
http://npdc.usda.gov/

University of Michigan Dearborn site for the uses of plants by Native Americans:
http://herb.umd.umich.edu/

Society for Economic Botany:
http://www.econbot.org/_welcome_/to_seb.php

Plant Conservation Alliance site with projects, medicinal and other plant uses:
http://www.nps.gov/plants/

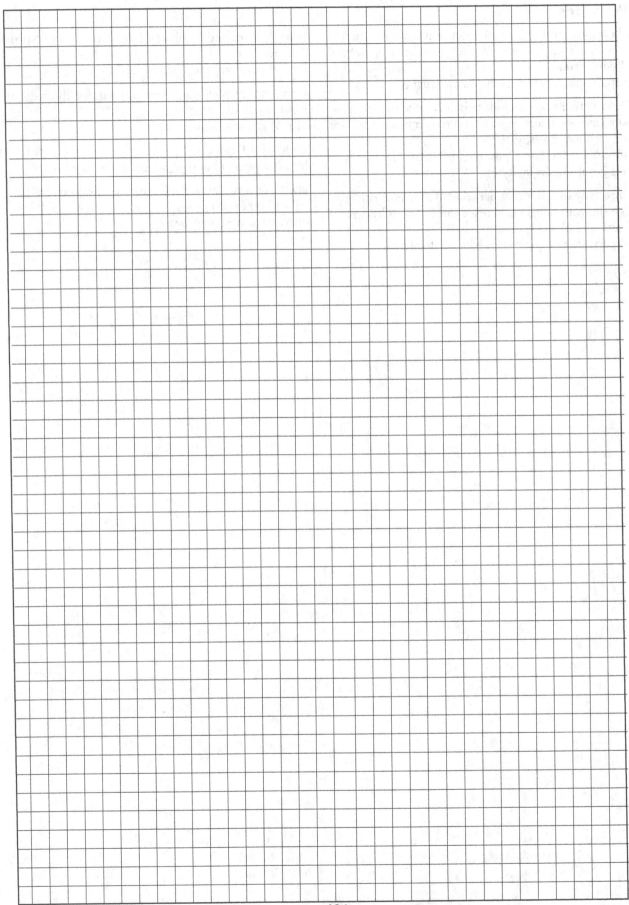

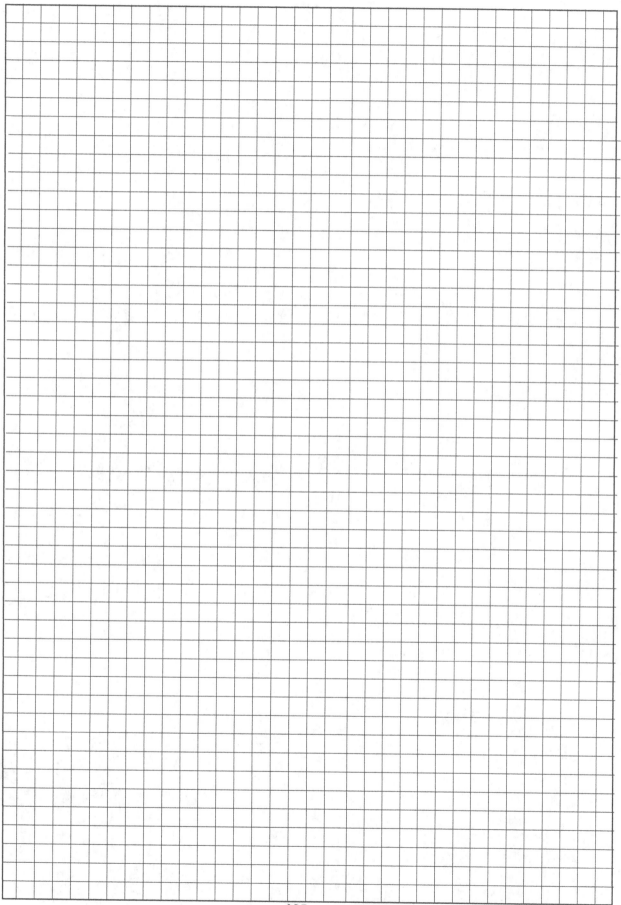

Animal Diversity: Porifera, Cnidaria, Platyhelminthes, Annelida, and Mollusca

Laboratory Objectives

After completing this lab topic, you should be able to:

1. Compare the anatomy of the representative animals, describing similarities and differences in organs and body form that allow the animal to carry out body functions.
2. Discuss the impact of molecular studies on traditional phylogenetic trees.
3. Discuss the relationship between body form and the lifestyle or niche of the organism.

Introduction

Animals are classified in the domain **Eukarya**, kingdom **Animalia** (clade Metazoa). They are multicellular organisms and are **heterotrophic**, meaning that they obtain food by ingesting other organisms or their by-products. Careful study of comparative anatomy, embryology, and most recently, genetic and molecular data, reveals many similarities in structure and development. Collectively, this evidence implies an ancestral evolutionary relationship among all animals. Animals are thought to have arisen about 575 million years ago, with most body forms appearing by the end of the Cambrian period. Scientists recognize over 35 major groups of present-day animals based on differences in body architecture. In this lab topic you will investigate body form and function in examples of nine major groups of animals. You will use these investigations to ask and answer questions comparing general features of morphology and relating these features to the lifestyle of each animal.

Since the beginning of the scientific study of animals, scientists have attempted to sort and group closely related organisms. Taxonomists have divided the metazoa into two major groups: **Parazoa**, which includes the sponges, and **Eumetazoa,**which includes all other animals. This division is made because the body form of sponges is so different from that of other animals that most biologists think that sponges are not closely related to any other animal groups.

Animals in Eumetazoa differ in physical characteristics, such as symmetry which may be **radial** (parts arranged around a central axis), or **bilateral** (right and left halves are mirror images). Other differences include the type of body cavity (coelom) and such basic embryological differences as the number of germ

From *Investigating Biology Laboratory Manual,* Sixth Edition, Judith G. Morgan and M. Eloise Brown Carter. Copyright © 2008 by Pearson Education, Inc. Published by Benjamin Cummings, Inc. All rights reserved.

layers present in the embryo and the embryonic development of the digestive tract. Some animals have a saclike body form with only one opening into a digestive cavity. Others have two outer openings, a mouth and an anus, and the digestive tract forms essentially a "tube within a tube." Those animals that are bilaterally symmetrical (clade Bilateria) are divided into two major groups, depending on differences in early development and the origin of the mouth and the anus. An embryonic structure, the blastopore, develops into a mouth in the **protostomes** and into an anus in the **deuterostomes.**

"Traditional" phylogenetic trees have been challenged by the results of molecular studies, particularly evidence from analysis of the gene coding for ribosomal RNA (rRNA). This is true not only for protists, but also for animals. Particularly in the protostomes, molecular studies have led to a regrouping of many traditionally established phylogenetic relationships. For example, for over 200 years zoology publications have assumed that annelids (segmented worms in the phylum Annelida) and arthropods (e.g., insects) are closely related based on their segmented bodies. Zoologists also noted, however, that annelids have developmental patterns similar to several groups that are not segmented. For example, annelids are like molluscs (e.g., clams) in having a developmental stage called the "trochophore larva." Recent molecular evidence helps to clarify this puzzle as it supports the hypothesis that annelids and molluscs are closely related, and separate from arthropods.

Molecular studies have led taxonomists to create two large groups within the protostomes, **Lophotrochozoa** and **Ecdysozoa.** Annelids, molluscs, and several more phyla not studied here are placed in the clade Lophotrochozoa. The name reflects the trochophore larvae found in annelids and molluscs. Also included in this clade are flatworms (phylum Platyhelminthes). Although flatworms lack such characteristics as a body cavity, the "tube-within-a-tube" body plan with mouth and anus, and elaborate internal organs, recent molecular evidence indicates that they should be grouped with annelids and molluscs in the Lophotrochozoa clade. Evidence from ribosomal DNA sequences indicates that roundworms or nematodes (phylum Nematoda), arthropods (phylum Arthropoda), and several other phyla belong in the clade Ecdysozoa. Animals in this clade undergo molting (ecdysis) or the shedding of an outer body cover. In nematodes this covering is called the **cuticle.** In arthropods the covering is the **exoskeleton.**

Another surprising result of rRNA and other molecular evidence is that the nature of the body cavity may not be a characteristic that indicates major phylogenetic branching. In traditional phylogenetic groupings, flatworms and nematodes were considered primitive, neither group having a true coelom. Ribosomal evidence has now moved nematodes to a different position with arthropods in the metazoan tree.

Figure 1a is a diagram showing organisms classified in the *traditional* organization of animal phylogeny. This phylogeny is based on *morphology* and *development.* Figure 1b is a diagram showing the *new molecular-based* phylogeny. The order of animals studied in this lab is based on Figure 1b, the molecular-based phylogeny. However, as you study the animals, note those morphological characteristics that were the basis of the traditional system of classification. These characteristics may give evidence of the influence of ecological events in the development of different morphologies. Be ready to discuss how these similarities or differences may have arisen secondarily or through secondary simplifications.

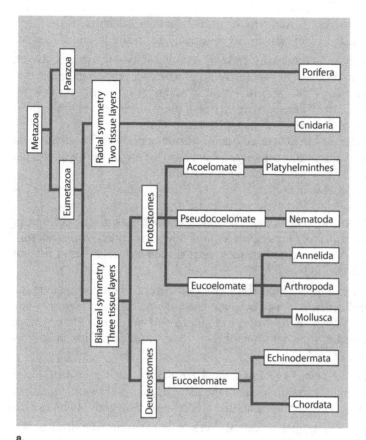

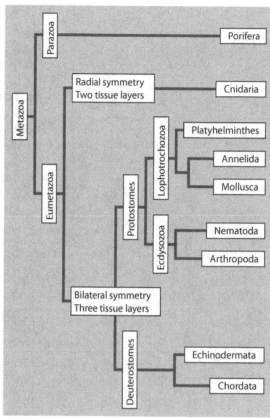

a.   **b.**

Figure 1.
Phylogenetic organization of animals.
(a) A traditional phylogeny based on morphology and embryology. (b) Proposed phylogeny based on new molecular evidence. Protostomes are grouped in Lophotrochozoa or Ecdysozoa.

Much work remains to resolve the branching order within the lophotrochozoan and ecdysozoan clades. Scientists are collecting evidence from studies based on mitochondrial DNA sequencing, ribosomal genes, *Hox* genes, and genes coding for various proteins.

The animals you will study in this lab are the sponge, hydra, planarian, clamworm, earthworm, and clam (mussel). As you study each animal, relate your observations to the unifying themes of this lab: *phylogenetic relationships* and criteria that are the basis for animal classification, the *relationship between form and function,* and the *relationship of the environment and lifestyle to form and function.* The questions at the end of the lab topics will help you do this.

In your comparative study of these organisms, you will investigate 13 characteristics. Before you begin the dissections, become familiar with the following characteristics and their descriptions:

1. *Symmetry.* Is the animal (a) radially symmetrical (parts arranged around a central axis), (b) bilaterally symmetrical (right and left halves are mirror images), or (c) asymmetrical (no apparent symmetry)?

2. *Tissue organization.* Are cells organized into well-defined tissue layers (structural and functional units)? How many distinctive layers are present?

3. *Body cavity.* Is a body cavity present? A body cavity—the space between the gut and body wall—is present only in three-layered organisms, that is, in organisms with the embryonic germ layers ectoderm, mesoderm, and endoderm. There are three types of body forms related to the presence of a body cavity and its type (Figure 2).
   a. Acoelomate, three-layered bodies without a body cavity. Tissue from the mesoderm fills the space where a cavity might be; therefore, the tissue layers closely pack on one another.
   b. Pseudocoelomate, three-layered bodies with a cavity between the endoderm (gut) and mesoderm (muscle).
   c. Eucoelomate (coelomate), three-layered bodies with the coelom, or cavity, *within* the mesoderm (completely surrounded by mesoderm). In coelomate organisms, mesodermal membranes suspend the gut within the body cavity.

4. *Openings into the digestive tract.* Can you detect where food enters the body and digestive waste exits the body? Some animals have only one opening, which serves as both a mouth and an anus. Others have a body called a "tube within a tube," with an anterior mouth and a posterior anus.

5. *Circulatory system.* Does this animal have open circulation (the blood flows through coelomic spaces in the tissue as well as in blood vessels), or does it have closed circulation (the blood flows entirely through vessels)?

6. *Habitat.* Is the animal terrestrial (lives on land) or aquatic (lives in water)? Aquatic animals may live in marine (sea) or fresh water.

7. *Organs for respiration (gas exchange).* Can you detect the surface where oxygen enters the body and carbon dioxide leaves the body? Many animals use their skin for respiration. Others have special organs, including gills in aquatic organisms and lungs in terrestrial organisms. Insects have a unique system for respiration, using structures called *spiracles* and *tracheae.*

8. *Organs for excretion.* How does the animal rid its body of nitrogenous waste? In many animals, these wastes pass out of the body through the skin by diffusion. In others, there are specialized structures, such as Malpighian tubules, lateral excretory canals, lateral canals with flame cells, structures called *nephridia,* and kidneys.

9. *Type of locomotion.* Does the organism swim, crawl on its belly, walk on legs, burrow in the substrate, or fly? Does it use cellular structures, such as cilia, to glide its body over the substrate?

10. *Support systems.* Is there a skeleton present? Is it an endoskeleton (inside the epidermis or skin of the animal), or is it an exoskeleton (outside the body wall)? Animals with no true skeleton can be supported by water: Fluid within and between cells and in body chambers such as a gastrovascular cavity or coelom provides a "hydrostatic skeleton."

11. *Segmentation.* Can you observe linear repetition of similar body parts? The repetition of similar units, or segments, is called *segmentation.* Segments can be more similar (as in the earthworm) or less similar (as in a lobster). Can you observe any degree of segmentation? Have various segments become modified for different functions?

12. *Appendages.* Are there appendages (organs or parts attached to a trunk or outer body wall)? Are these appendages all along the length of the

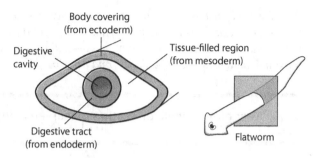

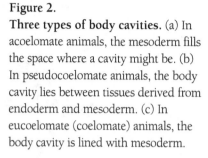

Figure 2.

Three types of body cavities. (a) In acoelomate animals, the mesoderm fills the space where a cavity might be. (b) In pseudocoelomate animals, the body cavity lies between tissues derived from endoderm and mesoderm. (c) In eucoelomate (coelomate) animals, the body cavity is lined with mesoderm.

a. Acoelomate

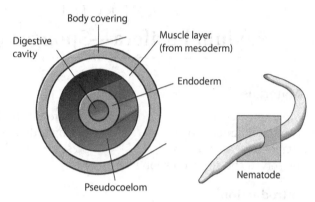

b. Pseudocoelomate

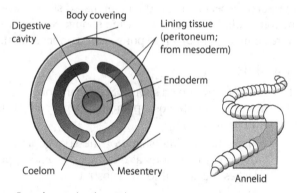

c. Eucoelomate (coelomate)

Adapted from N. Campbell, *Biology*, 4th ed. (Menlo Park, CA: Benjamin/Cummings, 1996), © 1996 The Benjamin/Cummings Publishing Company.

body, or are they restricted to one area? Are they all similar, or are they modified for different functions?

13. *Type of nervous system.* Do you see a brain and nerve cord? Is there more than one nerve cord? What is the location of the nerve cord(s)? Are sensory organs or structures present? Where and how many? What purpose do such structures serve (for example, eyes for light detection)?

As you carefully study or dissect each organism, refer to these thirteen characteristics, observe the animal, and record your observations in the summary table. You may find it helpful to make sketches of difficult structures or dissections in the margin of your lab manual for future reference.

Before you begin this study, become thoroughly familiar with dissection techniques, orientation terms, and planes and sections of the body. Be able to use the terms associated with bilateral symmetry—anterior, posterior, dorsal, ventral, proximal, and distal—as you dissect and describe your animals.

 Wear gloves while dissecting preserved animals.

EXERCISE 1
Phylum Porifera—Sponges (*Scypha*)

Materials

dissecting needle
compound microscope
stereoscopic microscope
preserved and dry bath sponges

prepared slide of *Scypha* in
   longitudinal section
preserved *Scypha* in watch glass

Introduction

Sponges are classified in a separate group, Parazoa, because of their unique body form. You will observe the unique sponge structure by observing first a preserved specimen and then a prepared slide of a section taken through the longitudinal axis of the marine sponge *Scypha*. You will observe other more complex and diverse sponges on demonstration.

Procedure

1. Obtain the preserved sponge *Scypha* and observe its external characteristics using the stereoscopic microscope, comparing your observations with Figure3a.

   a. Note the vaselike shape of the sponge and the **osculum,** a large opening to the body at one end. The end opposite the osculum attaches the animal to the substrate.

   b. Note the invaginations in the body wall, which form numerous folds and channels. You may be able to observe needlelike **spicules** around the osculum and protruding from the surface of the body. These spicules are made of calcium carbonate: They give support and protection to the sponge body and prevent small animals from entering the sponge's internal cavity.

2. Using the compound microscope, examine a prepared slide of a sponge body in longitudinal section and compare it with Figure 3b.

   a. Again, locate the osculum. This structure is not a mouth, as its name implies, but an opening used as an outlet for the current of water passing through the body wall and the **central cavity,** or **spongocoel.** The water enters the central cavity from channels and pores in the body. The central cavity is not a digestive tube or body cavity, but is only a channel for water.

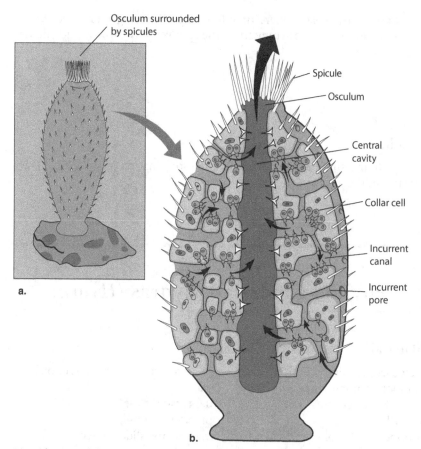

Osculum surrounded by spicules

Spicule

Osculum

Central cavity

Collar cell

Incurrent canal

Incurrent pore

a.

b.

Figure 3.

The sponge *Scypha.* (a) The entire sponge; (b) a longitudinal section through the sponge.

Adapted from L. Mitchell, J. Mutchmor, and W. Dolphin, *Zoology* (Menlo Park, CA: Benjamin/Cummings, 1988), © 1988 The Benjamin/Cummings Publishing Company.

b. Note the structure of the body wall. Are cells organized into definite tissue layers, or are they best described as a loose organization of various cell types? Various cells in the body wall carry out the functions of digestion, contractility, secretion of the spicules, and reproduction (some cells develop into sperm and eggs). One cell type unique to sponges is the **choanocyte,** or **collar cell.** These cells line the central cavity and the channels leading into it. Each collar cell has a flagellum extending from its surface. The collective beating of all flagella moves water through the sponge body. Small food particles taken up and digested by collar cells are one major source of nutrition for the sponge. How would you hypothesize about the movement of oxygen and waste throughout the sponge body and into and out of cells?

3. Observe examples of more complex sponges on demonstration. The body of these sponges, sometimes called "bath sponges," contains a complex series of large and small canals and chambers. The same cells that were described in *Scypha* are present in bath sponges, but, in addition to spicules, there is supportive material that consists of a soft proteinaceous substance called **spongin.** These sponges often grow to fit the

shape of the space where they live, and observing them gives you a good clue about the symmetry of the sponge body. How would you describe it?

Results

Complete the summary table, filling in all information for sponge characteristics in the appropriate row.

EXERCISE 2
Phylum Cnidaria—Hydras (*Hydra*)

Materials

stereoscopic microscope
compound microscope
living *Hydra* culture
water flea culture
dropper bottles of water, 1% acetic
  acid, and methylene blue

prepared slide of *Hydra* sections
watch glass
depression slide
pipettes and bulbs
microscope slide and coverslip

Introduction

Cnidarians are a diverse group of organisms, all of which have a **tissue grade** of organization, meaning that tissues, but no complex organs, are present. Included in this group are corals, jellies, sea anemones, and Portuguese men-of-war. Most species are marine; however, there are a few freshwater species. Two body forms are present in the life cycle of many of these animals—an umbrella-like, free-swimming stage, and a cylindrical, attached or stationary form. The stationary forms often grow into colonies of individuals. In this exercise you will observe some of the unique features of this group by observing the solitary, freshwater organism *Hydra*.

Procedure

1. Place several drops of freshwater pond or culture water in a watch glass or depression slide. Use a dropper to obtain a living hydra from the class culture, and place the hydra in the drop of water. Using a stereoscopic microscope, observe the hydra structure and compare it with Figure 4a. Note any movement, the symmetry, and any body structures present. Note the **tentacles** that surround the "mouth," the only opening into the central cavity. Tentacles are used in capturing food and in performing a certain type of locomotion, much like a "handspring." To accomplish this

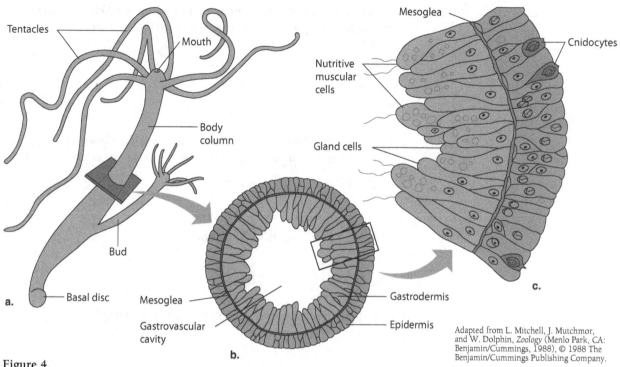

Figure 4.

Hydra. (a) A whole mount of *Hydra;* (b) enlargement showing a cross section through the body wall, revealing two tissue layers; and (c) further enlargement showing details of specialized cells in the body wall, including cnidocytes.

Adapted from L. Mitchell, J. Mutchmor, and W. Dolphin, *Zoology* (Menlo Park, CA: Benjamin/Cummings, 1988), © 1988 The Benjamin/Cummings Publishing Company.

motion, the hydra attaches its tentacles to the substrate and flips the basal portion of its body completely over, reattaching the base to a new position. If water fleas (*Daphnia*) are available, place one or two near the tentacles of the hydra and note the hydra's behavior. Set aside the hydra in the depression slide and return to it in a few moments.

2. Study a prepared slide of *Hydra* sections using the compound microscope and compare your observations with Figure 4b and 4c.

   Are definite tissue layers present? If so, how many?

   Given what you know of embryology, what embryonic layers would you guess give rise to the tissue layers of this animal's body?

3. Not visible with the microscope is a network of nerve cells in the body wall, which serves as the nervous system. There is no concentration of nerve cells into any kind of brain or nerve cord.

4. Observe the central cavity, called a **gastrovascular cavity.** Digestion begins in this water-filled cavity (**extracellular digestion**), but many food particles are drawn into cells in the **gastrodermis** lining the cavity, where **intracellular digestion** occurs.

5. Do you see signs of a skeleton or supportive system? How do you think the body is supported? Are appendages present?

6. Recalling the whole organism and observing this cross section, are organs for gas exchange present? How is gas exchange accomplished?

7. Do you see any organs for excretion?

8. Are specialized cell types seen in the layers of tissues?

Cnidarians have a unique cell type called **cnidocytes,** which contain a stinging organelle called a **nematocyst.** When stimulated, the nematocyst will evert from the cnidocyte with explosive force, trapping food or stinging predators. Look for these cells.

9. To better observe cnidocytes and nematocysts, turn your attention again to your living hydra and follow this procedure:

   a. Using a pipette, transfer the hydra to a drop of water on a microscope slide and carefully add a coverslip.

   b. Use your microscope to examine the hydra, first on low, then intermediate, and finally on high powers, focusing primarily on the tentacles. The cnidocytes will appear as swellings. If your microscope is equipped with phase contrast, switch to phase. Alternatively, add a drop of methylene blue to the edge of the coverslip. Locate several cnidocytes with nematocysts coiled inside.

   c. Add a drop of 1% acetic acid to the edge of the coverslip and, watching carefully using intermediate power, observe the rapid discharge of the nematocyst from the cnidocyte.

   d. Using high power, study the discharged nematocysts that will appear as long threads, often with large spines, or barbs, at the base of the thread.

Results

Complete the summary table, recording all information for *Hydra* characteristics in the appropriate row.

Discussion

What major differences have you detected between *Scypha* and *Hydra* body forms? List and describe them.

 Student Media Videos—Ch. 33: *Hydra* Building; *Hydra* Eating *Daphnia*; Jelly Swimming; Thimble Jellies

EXERCISE 3

Phylum Platyhelminthes— Planarians (*Dugesia*)

Materials

stereoscopic microscope
compound microscope
living planarian
watch glass

prepared slide of whole mount of planarian
prepared slide of planarian cross sections

Introduction

The phylum Platyhelminthes (clade Lophotrochozoa) includes planarians, free-living flatworms; that is, they are not parasitic and their body is dorsoventrally flattened. They are found under rocks, leaves, and debris in freshwater ponds and creeks. They move over these surfaces using a combination of muscles in their body wall and cilia on their ventral sides.

Procedure

1. Add a dropperful of pond or culture water to a watch glass. Use a dropper to obtain a living planarian from the class culture. Using your stereoscopic microscope, observe the planarian. Describe its locomotion. Is it directional? What is the position of its head? Does its body appear to contract?

As you observe the living planarian, you will see two striking new features with regard to symmetry that you did not see in the two phyla previously studied. What are they?

2. Add a *small* piece of fresh liver to the water near the planarian. The planarian may approach the liver and begin to feed by extending a long tubular **pharynx** out of the **mouth**, a circular opening on the ventral side of the body. If the planarian feeds, it will curve its body over the liver and extend the pharynx, which may be visible in the stereoscopic microscope.

   After observing the planarian's feeding behavior, return it to the culture dish, if possible, without the liver.

3. Using the lowest power on the compound microscope, observe the prepared slide of a whole planarian and compare it with Figure 5.

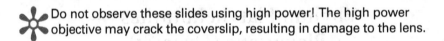 Do not observe these slides using high power! The high power objective may crack the coverslip, resulting in damage to the lens.

Examine the body for possible digestive tract openings. How many openings to the digestive tract are present?

Observe again the pharynx and the mouth. The pharynx lies in a **pharyngeal chamber** inside the mouth. The proximal end of the pharynx opens into a dark-colored, branched intestine. If the intestine has been stained on your slide, you will see the branching more easily.

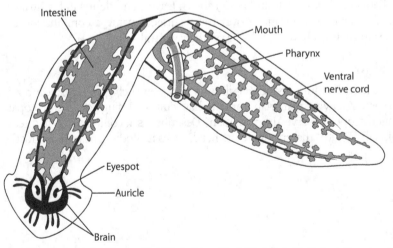

Figure 5.
A planarian. The digestive system consists of a mouth, a pharynx, and a branched intestine. A brain and two ventral nerve cords (plus transverse nerves connecting them, not shown) make up the nervous system.

Adapted from N. Campbell, J. Reece, and L. Mitchell, *Biology*, 5th ed. (Menlo Park, CA: Benjamin/Cummings, 1999), © 1999 The Benjamin/Cummings Publishing Company.

4. Continue your study of the whole planarian. The anterior blunt end of the animal is the head end. At each side of the head is a projecting **auricle.** It contains a variety of sensory cells, chiefly of touch and chemical sense. Between the two auricles on the dorsal surface are two pigmented **eyespots.** These are pigment cups into which retinal cells extend from the brain, with the photosensitive end of the cells inside the cup. Eyespots are sensitive to light intensities and the direction of a light source but can form no images. Beneath the eyespots are two cerebral ganglia that serve as the **brain.** Two ventral nerve cords extend posteriorly from the brain. These are connected by transverse nerves to form a ladderlike **nervous system.**

5. Study the prepared slide of cross sections of a planarian. You will have several sections on one slide. One section should have been taken at the level of the pharynx and pharyngeal chamber. Do you see a body cavity in any of the sections? (The pharyngeal chamber and spaces in the gut are not a body cavity.) What word describes this body cavity condition (see Figure 2a)?

   a. How many tissue layers can be detected? Speculate about their embryonic origin.

   Flatworms are the first group of animals to have three well-defined embryonic tissue layers, enabling them to have a variety of tissues and organs. Reproductive organs and excretory organs consisting of two lateral excretory canals and "flame cells" that move fluid through the canals are derived from the embryonic mesoderm. Respiratory, circulatory, and skeletal systems are lacking.

   b. How do you think the body is supported?

   c. How does gas exchange take place?

Results

1. Diagram the flatworm as seen in a cross section at the level of the pharynx. Label the **epidermis, muscle** derived from **mesoderm,** the lining of the digestive tract derived from **endoderm,** the **pharynx,** and the **pharyngeal chamber.**

2. Complete the summary table, recording all information for planarian characteristics in the appropriate row.

Discussion

One of the major differences between Cnidaria and Platyhelminthes is radial versus bilateral symmetry. Discuss the advantage of radial symmetry for sessile (attached) animals and bilateral symmetry for motile animals.

EXERCISE 4

Phylum Annelida—Clamworms (*Nereis*) and Earthworms (*Lumbricus terrestris*)

The phylum Annelida (clade Lophotrochozoa) includes a diverse group of organisms inhabiting a variety of environments. Examples range in size from microscopic to several meters in length. Most species are marine, living free in the open ocean or burrowing in ocean bottoms. Others live in fresh water or in soils. One group of annelids, the leeches, are parasitic and live on the blood or tissues of their hosts. In this exercise, you will study the clamworm, a marine annelid, and the earthworm, a terrestrial species. Keep in mind features that are adaptations to marine and terrestrial habitats as you study these organisms.

Lab Study A. Clamworms (*Nereis*)

Materials

dissecting tools
dissecting pan
preserved clamworm

disposable gloves
dissecting pins

Introduction

Species of *Nereis* (clamworms) are commonly found in mud flats and on the ocean floor. These animals burrow in sediments during the day and emerge to feed at night. As you observe the clamworm, note features that are characteristic of all annelids, as well as features that are special adaptations to the marine environment.

Procedure

1. Observe the preserved, undissected clamworm and compare it with Figure 6. How would you describe the symmetry of this organism?

2. Determine the anterior and posterior ends. At the anterior end, the well-differentiated head bears **sensory appendages.** Locate the mouth, which leads into the digestive tract.

3. A conspicuous new feature of these organisms is the presence of **segmentation,** the division of the body along its length into segments. Posterior to the head region, the segments bear fleshy outgrowths called **parapodia.** Each parapodium contains several terminal bristles called **setae.** In Lab Study B, you will see that the earthworm has setae but does not have parapodia. Suggest functions for parapodia and setae in the marine clamworm.

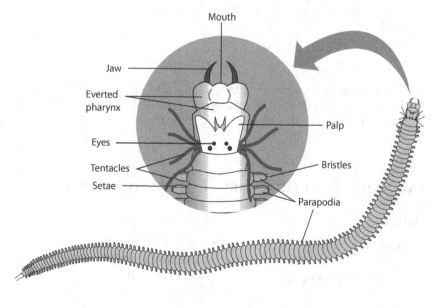

Figure 6.
The clamworm, *Nereis*. The head has sensory appendages, and each segment of the body bears two parapodia with setae.

4. Holding the animal in your hand and using sharp-pointed scissors, make a middorsal incision the full length of the body. Carefully insert the tip of the scissors and lift up with the tips as you cut. Pin the opened body in the dissecting pan but do not put pins through the head region.

5. Locate the **intestine.** Do you see the "tube-within-a-tube" body plan?

6. Two **muscle layers,** one inside the skin and a second lying on the surface of the intestine, may be visible with the stereoscopic microscope. With muscle in these two positions, what kind of coelom does this animal have (see Figure 2c)?

7. Continuing your observations with the unaided eye and the stereoscopic microscope, look for **blood vessels,** particularly a large vessel lying on the dorsal wall of the digestive tract. This vessel is contractile and propels the blood throughout the body. You should be able to observe smaller lateral blood vessels connecting the dorsal blood vessel with another on the ventral side of the intestine. As you will see, in the earthworm these connecting vessels are slightly enlarged as "hearts" around the anterior portion of the digestive tract (around the esophagus). This is not as obvious in *Nereis.* What is this type of circulatory system, with blood circulating through continuous closed vessels?

8. Gas exchange must take place across wet, thin surfaces. Do you see any organs for gas exchange (gills or lungs, for example)? How do you suspect that gas exchange takes place?

9. Do you see any signs of a skeleton? What would serve as support for the body?

10. Clamworms and earthworms have a small bilobed brain (a pair of ganglia) lying on the surface of the digestive tract at the anterior end of the worm. You can see this more easily in an earthworm.

Lab Study B. Earthworms (*Lumbricus terrestris*)

Materials

dissecting instruments	preserved earthworm
compound microscope	prepared slide of cross section
stereoscopic microscope	of earthworm

Introduction

Lumbricus species, commonly called *earthworms,* burrow through soils rich in organic matter. As you observe these animals, note features that are adaptations to the burrowing, terrestrial lifestyle.

Procedure

1. Obtain a preserved earthworm and identify its anterior end by locating the mouth, which is overhung by a fleshy dorsal protuberance called the **prostomium.** The anus at the posterior end has no such protuberance. Also, a swollen glandular band, the **clitellum** (a structure that secretes a cocoon that holds eggs), is located closer to the mouth than to the anus (Figure 7).

   a. Using scissors, make a middorsal incision along the anterior third of the animal, as you did for *Nereis.* You can identify the dorsal surface in a couple of ways. The prostomium is dorsal, and the ventral surface of the worm is usually flattened, especially in the region of the clitellum. Cut to the prostomium. Pin the body open in a dissecting pan near the edge. You may need to cut through the septa that divide the body cavity into segments.

   b. Using a stereoscopic microscope or hand lens, look for the small **brain** just behind the prostomium on the surface of the digestive tract. Note the two nerves that pass from the brain around the pharynx and meet ventrally. These nerve tracts continue posteriorly as a **ventral nerve cord** lying in the floor of the coelom.

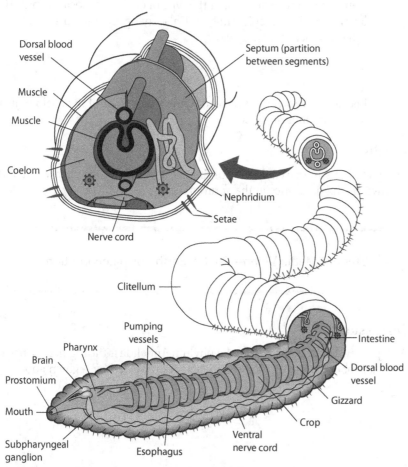

Dorsal blood vessel

Muscle

Muscle

Coelom

Nerve cord

Septum (partition between segments)

Nephridium

Setae

Clitellum

Pumping vessels

Pharynx

Brain

Prostomium

Mouth

Subpharyngeal ganglion

Esophagus

Ventral nerve cord

Crop

Gizzard

Dorsal blood vessel

Intestine

Adapted from N. Campbell, J. Reece, and L. Mitchell, *Biology,* 5th ed. (Menlo Park, CA: Benjamin/Cummings, 1999), © 1999 The Benjamin/Cummings Publishing Company.

Figure 7.
The earthworm. The small brain leads to a ventral nerve cord. A pair of nephridia lie in each segment.

c. Look for the large **blood vessel** on the dorsal wall of the digestive tract. You may be able to see the enlarged lateral blood vessels (**hearts**) around the anterior portion of the digestive tract.

d. Identify (from anterior to posterior) the **pharynx, esophagus, crop** (a soft, swollen region of the digestive tract), **gizzard** (smaller and more rigid than the crop), and **intestine.**

e. Excretion in the clamworm and earthworm is carried out by organs called **nephridia.** A pair of these minute, white, coiled tubes is located in each segment of the worm body. Nephridia are more easily observed in the earthworm than in *Nereis* and should be studied here. To view these organs, cut out an approximately 2-cm-long piece of the worm posterior to the clitellum and cut it open along its dorsal surface. Cut through the septa and pin the piece to the dissecting pan near the edge to facilitate observation with the stereoscopic microscope. The coiled tubules of the nephridia are located in the coelomic cavity, where waste is collected and discharged to the outside through a small pore.

2. Using the compound microscope, observe the prepared slide of a cross section of the earthworm.

a. Locate the **thin cuticle** lying outside of and secreted by the **epidermis.** Recall the habitat of this organism and speculate about the function of the cuticle.

b. Confirm your decision about the type of coelom by locating **muscle layers** inside the epidermis and also lying on the surface of the **intestine** near the body cavity.

c. Locate the **ventral nerve cord,** lying in the floor of the coelom, just inside the muscle layer.

Results

Complete the summary table, recording all information for clamworm and earthworm characteristics in the appropriate row.

 Student Media Video—Ch. 33: Earthworm Locomotion

Discussion

A major new feature observed in the phylum Annelida is the segmented body. Speculate about possible adaptive advantages provided by segmentation.

EXERCISE 5
Phylum Mollusca—Clams

Materials

dissecting instruments
dissecting pan

preserved clam or mussel
disposable gloves

Introduction

Second only to the phylum Arthropoda in numbers of species, the phylum Mollusca (clade Lophotrochozoa) includes thousands of species living in many diverse habitats. Most species are marine. Others live in fresh water or on land. Many mollusks are of economic importance, being favorite human foods. Mollusks include such diverse animals as snails, slugs, clams, squids, and octopuses. Although appearing diverse, most of these animals share four characteristic features: (1) a hard external **shell** for protection; (2) a thin structure called the **mantle**, which secretes the shell; (3) a **visceral mass** in which most organs are located; and (4) a muscular **foot** used for locomotion.

In this exercise, you will dissect a clam, a molluscan species with a shell made of two parts called **valves.** Most clams are marine, although many genera live in freshwater lakes and ponds.

 Wear gloves while dissecting preserved animals.

Procedure

1. Observe the external anatomy of the preserved clam. Certain characteristics will become obvious immediately. Can you determine symmetry, support systems, and the presence or absence of appendages? Are there external signs of segmentation? Record observations.

2. Before you continue making observations, determine the dorsal, ventral, anterior, posterior, right, and left regions of the animal. Identify the two valves. The valves are held together by a **hinge** near the **umbo**, a hump on the valves. The hinge and the umbo are located **dorsally,** and the valves open **ventrally.** The umbo is displaced **anteriorly.** Hold the clam vertically with the umbo away from your body, and cup one of your hands over each valve. The valve in your right hand is the right valve; the valve in your left hand is the left valve. The two valves are held together by two strong **adductor** muscles inside the shell. Compare your observations with Figure 8.

 Be cautious as you open the clam! Hold the clam in the dissecting pan in such a way that the scalpel will be directed toward the bottom of the pan.

Figure 8.

Anatomy of a clam. The soft body parts are protected by the shell valves. Two adductor muscles hold the valves closed. Most major organs are located in the visceral mass. In this diagram, the left mantle, left pair of gills, and half of the visceral mass have been removed.

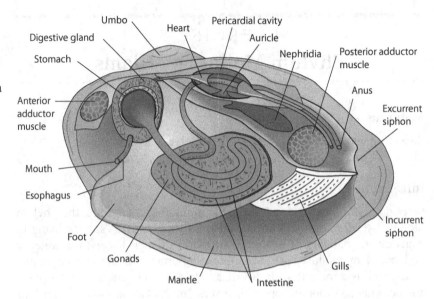

3. To study the internal anatomy of the clam, you must open it by prying open the valves. (A wooden peg may have been inserted between the two valves.) Insert the handle of your forceps or scalpel between the valves and twist it to pry the valves farther open. Carefully insert a scalpel blade, directed toward the dorsal side of the animal, into the space between the left valve and a flap of tissue lining the valve. The blade edge should be just ventral to (that is, below) the anterior adductor muscle (see Figure 8). The flap of tissue is the left **mantle.** Keeping the scalpel blade pressed flat against the left valve, carefully loosen the mantle from the valve and press the blade dorsally. You will feel the tough **anterior adductor muscle.** Cut through this muscle near the valve.

4. Repeat the procedure at the posterior end and cut the posterior adductor muscle. Lay the clam on its right valve and carefully lift the left valve. As you do this, use your scalpel to loosen the mantle from the valve. If you have been successful, you should have the body of the clam lying in the right valve. It should be covered by the mantle. Look for pearls between the mantle and the shell. How do you think pearls are formed?

5. Look at the posterior end of the animal where the left and right mantle come together. Hold the two mantle flaps together and note the two gaps formed. These gaps are called **incurrent** (ventral) and **excurrent** (dorsal) **siphons.** Speculate about the function of these siphons.

6. Lift the mantle and identify the **visceral mass** and the **muscular foot.**

7. Locate the **gills,** which have a pleated appearance. One function of these structures is obvious, but they have a second function as well. As water comes into the body (how would it get in?), it passes through the gills, and food particles are trapped on the gill surface. The food is then moved anteriorly (toward the mouth) by coordinated ciliary movements.

8. Locate the **mouth** between two flaps of tissue just ventral to the anterior adductor muscle. Look just above the posterior adductor muscle and locate the **anus.** How is it oriented in relation to the excurrent siphon?

9. Imagine that this is the first time you have seen a clam. From the observations you have made, what evidence would indicate whether this animal is aquatic or terrestrial?

10. The **heart** of the clam is located in a sinus, or cavity, just inside the hinge, dorsal to the visceral mass (see Figure 8). This cavity, called the *pericardial cavity,* is a reduced **true coelom.** The single ventricle of the heart actually surrounds the **intestine** passing through this cavity. Thin auricles, usually torn away during the dissection, empty into the heart via openings called **ostia.** Blood passes from **sinuses** in the body into the auricles. What type of circulatory system is this?

11. Ventral to the heart and embedded in mantle tissue are a pair of greenish brown tissue masses, the **nephridia,** or kidneys. The kidneys remove waste from the pericardial cavity.

12. Open the visceral mass by making an incision with the scalpel, dividing the mass into right and left halves. Begin this incision just above the foot and cut dorsally. You should be able to open the flap produced by this cut and see organs such as the **gonads, digestive gland, intestine,** and **stomach.** Clam chowder is made by chopping up the visceral mass.

13. It is difficult to observe the nervous system in the clam. It consists of three ganglia, one near the mouth, one in the foot, and one below the posterior adductor muscle. These ganglia are connected by nerves.

Now that you have dissected the clam, you should have concluded that there is no sign of true segmentation. Also, appendages (attached to a trunk or body wall) are absent.

Results

Complete the Summary Table, recording all information for clam characteristics in the appropriate row.

Discussion

List several features of clam anatomy that enable it to survive in a marine environment.

By the end of today's laboratory period, you should have completed observations of all animals described.

Applying Your Knowledge

A hydra (*Chlorophyra viridissima*) is bright green, and yet it does not synthesize chlorophyll. Think about the structure of the hydra and its feeding and digestive habits. What do you think is the origin of the green pigment in this species?

Investigative Extensions

1. Earthworms are among the most familiar inhabitants of soil. They play an important role in improving the texture and adding organic matter to soil. You may have read Darwin's estimate that over 50,000 earthworms may inhabit one acre of British farmland. Earthworms are readily available from biological supply houses, or you may collect your own to use in experiments. Following are questions that you might investigate.

   a. Why do earthworms come out of their burrows when it rains? Is it because they may drown in the water in their burrows? Does rain stimulate mating behavior and are the worms coming to the surface to mate? Does the pH of the soil change as it rains, and is the burrow becoming too acidic or alkaline? What is the optimum pH range for earthworms? Does rain create conditions more favorable for migration to new habitats?

   b. What effects do chemicals used in agriculture have on earthworm populations? Compare numbers and health of earthworms in containers of soil to which varying amounts of fertilizers, pesticides, or herbicides have been added.

   c. Do earthworms in the soil stimulate plant growth? Compare the biomass of plants grown in containers with and without earthworms present.

2. An amazing diversity of organisms has evolved from the foot-mantle-visceral mass body plan of mollusks. Living terrestrial, freshwater, and marine snails and bivalves are available from biological supply houses, aquarium supply stores, or from ponds or terrestrial sites in your area. Consider the following questions that you might investigate. (A Google search for "snail experiments" yields over 1,140,000 entries, including experiments being performed in the International Space Station.)

   a. What effect does sedimentation have on aquatic snail populations? Consider changes in water chemistry and/or substrate.

   b. What effect does temperature have on the growth and/or reproduction of aquatic or terrestrial snails or slugs? Why would this question be of interest?

   c. Invasive aquatic plants have become a major concern of scientists worldwide. For example, water hyacinth, introduced into ponds in the southern U.S., chokes ponds and waterways, in some cases hindering human and fish navigation. Ponds may become so choked that they dry up, destroying habitat for alligators, turtles, fish, and other native species. Design a greenhouse experiment to test the efficacy of aquatic snails in controlling the growth of invasive aquatic plants.

 ## Student Media Activities and Investigations

Activities—Ch. 32: Animal Phylogenetic Tree; Ch. 33: Characteristics of Invertebrates
Investigations—Ch. 32: How Do Molecular Data Fit Traditional Phylogenies?
www.masteringbio.com

References

Adoutte, A., G. Balavoine, N. Lartillot, O. Lespinet, B. Prud'homme, and R. de Rosa. "The New Animal Phylogeny: Reliability and Implications." *Proc. Natl. Acad. Sci.* USA, 2000, vol. 97, no. 9, pp. 4453–4456.

Balavoine, G. "Are Platyhelminthes Coelomates Without a Coelom? An Argument Based on the Evolution of Hox Genes." *American Zoologist,* 1989, vol. 38, pp. 843–858.

Erwin, D., J. Valentine, and D. Jablonski. "The Origin of Animal Body Plans." *American Scientist,* 1997, vol. 85, pp. 126–137.

Mallatt, J. and C. Winchell. "Testing the New Animal Phylogeny: First Use of Combined Large-Subunit and Small-Subunit rRNA Sequences to Classify Protostomes." *Molecular Biology and Evolution,* 2002, vol. 19, pp. 289–301.

Websites

Includes descriptions of many invertebrates and vertebrates, links to insect keys, references:
http://animaldiversity.ummz.umich.edu/site/index.html

The Tree of Life web project provides information on all major groups of organisms, including invertebrates:
http://tolweb.org/Bilateria

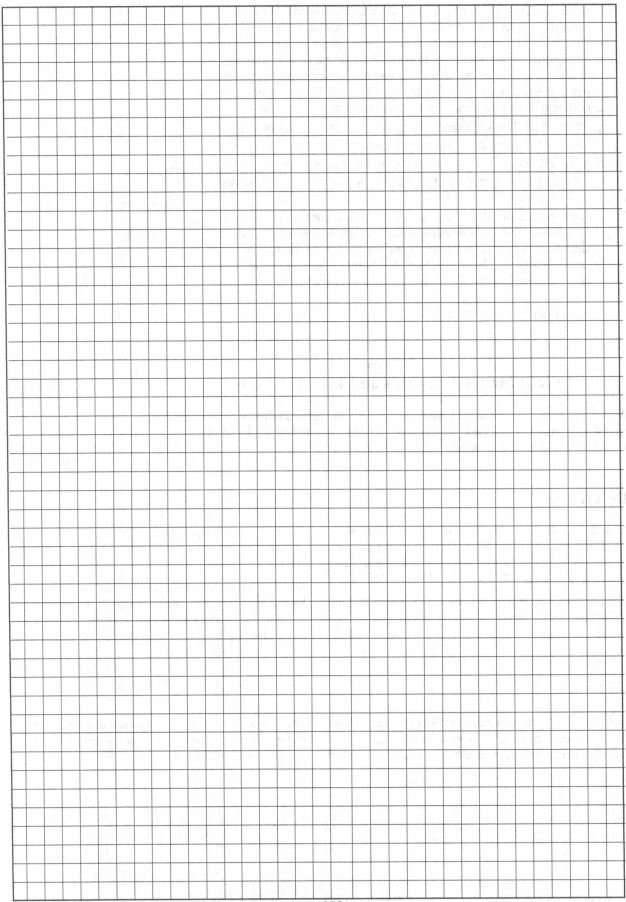

Animal Diversity: Nematoda, Arthropoda, Echinodermata, and Chordata

In this lab topic you will study examples of two protostome phyla included in the clade **Ecdysozoa**, Nematoda (Exercise 1) and Arthropoda (Exercise 2). Recall that these organisms have coverings on their body surfaces. In Exercises 3 and 4, you will study two deuterostome phyla, Echinodermata and Chordata.

As you continue your study of representative organisms, continue to record your observations in Table 1 at the end of this lab topic. Keep in mind the big themes you are investigating.

1. What clues do similarities and differences among organisms provide about phylogenetic relationships?
2. How is body form related to function?
3. How is body form related to environment and lifestyle?
4. What characteristics can be the criteria for major branching points in producing a phylogenetic tree (representing animal classification)?

EXERCISE 1
Phylum Nematoda— Roundworms (*Ascaris*)

Materials

dissecting instruments
dissecting pan
dissecting pins
compound microscope
disposable gloves

preserved *Ascaris*
prepared slide of cross section
   of *Ascaris*
hand lens (optional)

From *Investigating Biology Laboratory Manual,* Sixth Edition, Judith G. Morgan and M. Eloise Brown Carter. Copyright © 2008 by Pearson Education, Inc. Published by Benjamin Cummings, Inc. All rights reserved.

Introduction

Roundworms, or nematodes (clade Ecdysozoa), are among the most abundant and resilient organisms on earth. NASA is using the nematode *Caenorhabditis elegans* in experiments to test the way weightlessness and space radiation affect an organism's genes. NASA has additional plans to launch worms into orbit aboard small satellites in the near future. *C. elegans* is a small roundworm—only one millimeter in length. *Ascaris,* the roundworm you will study in this exercise, is considerably larger.

Ascaris lives as a parasite in the intestines of mammals such as horses, pigs, and humans. Recall that ecdysozoans secrete exoskeletons that must be shed as the animal grows. Nematodes are covered with a proteinaceous **cuticle** that sheds periodically. Most often these parasites are introduced into the mammalian body when food contaminated with nematode eggs is eaten. Keep in mind the problem of adaptation to a parasitic lifestyle as you study the structure of this animal.

 Wear disposable gloves while dissecting preserved animals.

Procedure

1. Wearing disposable gloves, obtain a preserved *Ascaris* and determine its sex. Females are generally larger than males. The posterior end of the male is sharply curved.

2. Use a hand lens or a stereoscopic microscope to look at the ends of the worm. A mouth is present at the anterior end. Three "lips" border this opening. A small slitlike **anus** is located ventrally near the posterior end of the animal.

3. Open the animal by making a middorsal incision along the length of the body with a sharp-pointed probe or sharp scissors. Remember that the anus is slightly to the ventral side (Figure 1). Be careful not to go too deep. Once the animal is open, pin the free edges of the body wall to the dissecting pan, spreading open the body. Pinning the animal near the edge of the pan will allow you to view it using the stereoscopic microscope. As you study the internal organs, you will note that there is a **body cavity.** This is not a true coelom, however, as you will see shortly when you study microscopic sections. From your observations, you should readily identify such characteristics as symmetry, tissue organization, and digestive tract openings.

    a. The most obvious organs you will see in the dissected worm are **reproductive organs,** which appear as masses of coiled tubules of varying diameters.

    b. Identify the flattened **digestive tract,** or intestine, extending from mouth to anus. This tract has been described as a "tube within a tube," the outer tube being the body wall.

    c. Locate two pale lines running laterally along the length of the body in the body wall. The excretory system consists of two longitudinal tubes lying in these two **lateral lines.**

    d. There are no organs for gas exchange or circulation. Most parasitic roundworms are essentially anaerobic (require no oxygen).

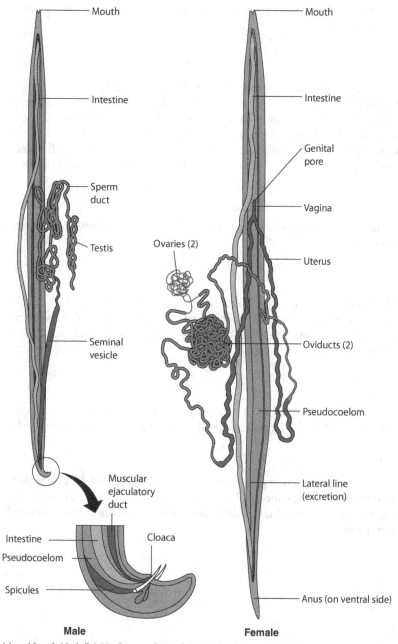

Figure 1.
Male and female *Ascaris*. The digestive tract originates at the mouth and terminates in the anus. Reproductive structures fill the body cavity.

Adapted from L. Mitchell, J. Mutchmor, and W. Dolphin, *Zoology* (Menlo Park, CA: Benjamin/Cummings, 1988), © 1988 The Benjamin/Cummings Publishing Company.

e. How would nourishment be taken into the body and be circulated?

f. The nervous system consists of a ring of nervous tissue around the anterior end of the worm, with one dorsal and one ventral nerve cord. These structures will be more easily observed in the prepared slide.

g. Do you see signs of segmentation in the body wall or in the digestive, reproductive, or excretory systems?

h. Do you see signs of a support system? What do you think supports the body?

4. Using the compound microscope, observe a prepared slide of a cross section through the body of a female worm. Note that the body wall is made up of (from outside inward) **cuticle** (noncellular), **epidermis** (cellular), and **muscle fibers.** The muscle (derived from mesoderm) lies at the outer boundary of the body cavity. Locate the **intestine** (derived from endoderm). Can you detect muscle tissue adjacent to the endodermal layer?

What do we call a coelom that is lined by mesoderm (outside) and endoderm (inside)?

5. Most of the body cavity is filled with reproductive organs. You should see cross sections of the two large **uteri,** sections of the coiled **oviducts** with small lumens, and many sections of the **ovaries** with no lumen. What do you see inside the uteri?

6. By carefully observing the cross section, you should be able to locate the **lateral lines** for excretion and the dorsal and ventral **nerve cords.**

Results

1. Sketch the cross section of a female *Ascaris.* Label the **cuticle, epidermis, muscle fibers, intestine, body cavity** (give specific name), **reproductive organs,** (uterus, oviduct, ovary), **lateral lines,** and **dorsal** and **ventral nerve cords.**

2. List some features of *Ascaris* that are possible adaptations to parasitic life.

3. Complete the summary table, Table 1, recording all information for roundworm characteristics in the appropriate row. You will use this information to complete Table 2 and answer questions in the Applying Your Knowledge section at the end of this lab topic.

 Student Media Video—Ch. 33: *C. elegans* Crawling

Discussion

1. Discuss the significance of an animal's having two separate openings to the digestive tract, as seen in *Ascaris*.

2. What are the advantages of a body cavity being present in an animal?

EXERCISE 2
Phylum Arthropoda

Organisms in the phylum Arthropoda (clade Ecdysozoa) have been very successful species. Evidence indicates that arthropods may have lived on Earth half a billion years ago. They can be found in almost every imaginable habitat: marine waters, fresh water, and almost every terrestrial niche. Many species are directly beneficial to humans, serving as a source of food. Others make humans miserable by eating their homes, infesting their domestic animals, eating their food, and biting their bodies. These organisms have an exoskeleton that periodically sheds as they grow. In this exercise, you will observe the morphology of two arthropods: the crayfish (an aquatic arthropod) and the grasshopper (a terrestrial arthropod).

Lab Study A. Crayfish (*Cambarus*)

Materials

dissecting instruments
dissecting pan

preserved crayfish
disposable gloves

155

Introduction

Crayfish live in streams, ponds, and swamps, usually protected under rocks and vegetation. They may walk slowly over the substrate of their habitat, but they can also swim rapidly using their tails. The segmentation seen in annelids is seen also in crayfish and all arthropods; however, you will see that the segments are grouped into functional units.

Procedure

1. Obtain a preserved crayfish, study its external anatomy, and compare your observations with Figure 2. Describe the body symmetry, supportive structures, appendages, and segmentation, and state the adaptive advantages of each characteristic.

   a. body symmetry

   b. supportive structures

   c. appendages

   d. segmentation

2. Identify the three regions of the crayfish body: the **head, thorax** (fused with the head), and **abdomen.** Note the appendages associated with each region. Speculate about the functions of each of these groups of appendages.

   a. head appendages

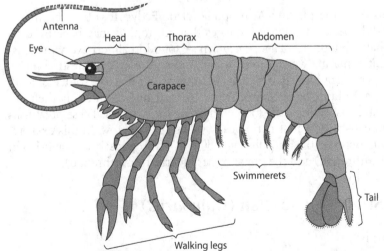

Figure 2.
External anatomy of a crayfish. The body is divided into head, thorax, and abdominal regions. Appendages grouped in a region perform specific functions.

Adapted from L. Mitchell, J. Mutchmor, and W. Dolphin, *Zoology* (Menlo Park, CA: Benjamin/Cummings, 1988), © 1988 The Benjamin/Cummings Publishing Company.

b. thoracic appendages

c. abdominal appendages

3. Feathery **gills** lie under the lateral extensions of a large, expanded exoskeletal plate called the **carapace** (see Figure 2). To expose the gills, use scissors to cut away a portion of the plate on the left side of the animal. What is the function of the gills? Speculate about how this function is performed.

4. Remove the dorsal portion of the carapace to observe other organs in the head and thorax. Compare your observations with Figure 3.

   a. Start on each side of the body at the posterior lateral edge of the carapace and make two lateral cuts extending along each side of the thorax and forward over the head, meeting just behind the eyes. This should create a dorsal flap in the carapace.

   b. Carefully insert a needle under this flap and separate the underlying tissues as you lift the flap.

   c. Observe the **heart,** a small, angular structure located just under the carapace near the posterior portion of the thorax. (If you were not successful in leaving the tissues behind as you removed the carapace, you may have removed the heart with the carapace.) Thin threads

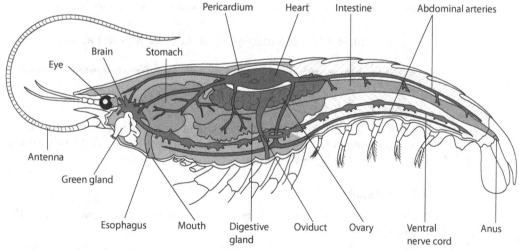

Adapted from L. Mitchell, J. Mutchmor, and W. Dolphin, *Zoology* (Menlo Park, CA: Benjamin/Cummings, 1988), © 1988 The Benjamin/Cummings Publishing Company.

Figure 3.

Internal anatomy of the crayfish. Large digestive glands fill much of the body cavity. The intestine extends from the stomach through the tail to the anus. The green glands lie near the brain in the head.

leading out from the heart are **arteries.** Look for holes in the heart wall. When blood collects in **sinuses** around the heart, the heart relaxes, and these holes open to allow the heart to fill with blood. The holes then close, and the blood is pumped through the arteries, which distribute it around the body. Blood seeps back to the heart, since no veins are present. What is the name given to this kind of circulation?

d. Locate the **stomach** in the head region. It is a large, saclike structure. It may be obscured by the large, white **digestive glands** that fill the body cavity inside the body wall. Leading posteriorly from the stomach is the **intestine.** Make longitudinal cuts through the exoskeleton on either side of the dorsal midline of the abdomen. Lift the exoskeleton and trace the intestine to the anus. (When shrimp are "deveined" in preparation for eating, the intestine is removed.) Given all of the organs and tissues around the digestive tract and inside the body wall in the body cavity, what kind of coelom do you think this animal has?

e. Turn your attention to the anterior end of the specimen again. Pull the stomach posteriorly (this will tear the esophagus) and look inside the most anterior portion of the head. Two **green glands** (they do not look green), the animal's excretory organs, are located in this region. These are actually long tubular structures that resemble nephridia but are compacted into a glandular mass. Waste and excess water pass from these glands to the outside of the body through pores at the base of the antennae on the head.

f. Observe the **brain** just anterior to the green glands. It lies in the midline with nerves extending posteriorly, fusing to form a **ventral nerve cord.**

 Student Media Video—Ch. 33: Lobster Mouth Parts

Results

Complete Table 1, recording all information for crayfish characteristics in the appropriate row. Use this information to complete Table 2 and answer questions in the Applying Your Knowledge section at the end of this lab topic.

Discussion

How does the pattern of segmentation differ in the crayfish and the earthworm?

Lab Study B. Grasshoppers (*Romalea*)

Materials

dissecting instruments   preserved grasshopper
dissecting pan   disposable gloves

Introduction

The grasshopper, an insect, is an example of a terrestrial arthropod. Insects are the most successful and abundant of all land animals. They are the principal invertebrates in dry environments, and they can survive extreme temperatures. They are the only invertebrates that can fly. As you study the grasshopper, compare the anatomy of this terrestrial animal with that of the aquatic crayfish, just studied. This comparison should suggest ways that terrestrial animals have solved the problems of life out of water.

Procedure

1. Observe the external anatomy of the grasshopper. Compare your observations with Figure 4.

   a. Note the symmetry, supportive structures, appendages, and segmentation of the grasshopper.

   b. Observe the body parts. The body is divided into three regions: the **head**, the **thorax** (to which the legs and wings are attached), and the **abdomen.** Examine the appendages on the head, speculate about their functions, and locate the mouth opening into the digestive tract.

   c. Turning your attention to the abdomen, locate small dots along each side. These dots are **spiracles,** small openings into elastic air tubes, or **tracheae,** that branch to all parts of the body and constitute the respiratory system of the grasshopper. This system of tubes brings oxygen directly to the cells of the body.

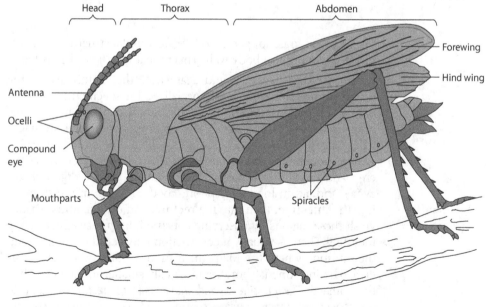

Head   Thorax   Abdomen

Forewing

Hind wing

Antenna

Ocelli

Compound eye

Mouthparts   Spiracles

Figure 4.
External anatomy of the grasshopper. The body is divided into head, thorax, and abdominal regions. Wings and large legs are present. Small openings, called *spiracles,* lead to internal tracheae, allowing air to pass into the body.

Adapted from L. Mitchell, J. Mutchmor, and W. Dolphin, *Zoology* (Menlo Park, CA: Benjamin/Cummings, 1988), © 1988 The Benjamin/Cummings Publishing Company.

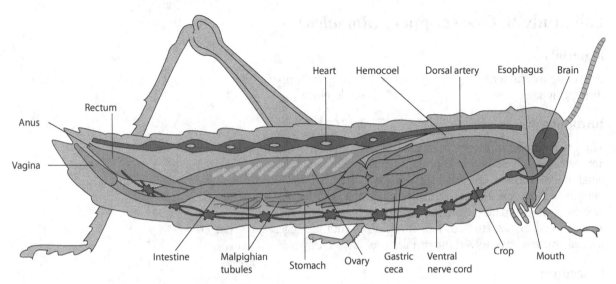

Figure 5.
Internal anatomy of the grasshopper. The digestive tract, extending from mouth to anus, is divided into specialized regions: the esophagus, crop, stomach, intestine, and rectum. Gastric ceca attach at the junction of the crop and the stomach. Malpighian tubules empty excretory waste into the anterior end of the intestine.

2. Remove the exoskeleton. First take off the wings and, starting at the posterior end, use scissors to make two lateral cuts toward the head. Remove the dorsal wall of the exoskeleton and note the segmented pattern in the muscles inside the body wall. Compare your observations with Figure 5 as you work.

   a. A space between the body wall and the digestive tract, the **hemocoel** (a true coelom), in life is filled with colorless blood. What type of circulation does the grasshopper have?

   The heart of a grasshopper is an elongate, tubular structure lying just inside the middorsal body wall. This probably will not be visible.

   b. Locate the digestive tract and again note the mouth. Along the length of the tract are regions specialized for specific functions. A narrow **esophagus** leading from the mouth expands into a large **crop** used for food storage. The crop empties into the **stomach**, where digestion takes place. Six pairs of fingerlike extensions called **gastric pouches** or **ceca** connect to the digestive tract where the crop and the stomach meet. These pouches secrete digestive enzymes and aid in food absorption. Food passes from the stomach into the **intestine,** then into the **rectum,** and out the **anus.** Distinguish these regions by observing constrictions and swellings along the tube. There is usually a constriction between the stomach and the intestine where the Malpighian tubules (discussed below) attach. The intestine is shorter and usually smaller in diameter than the stomach. *The intestine expands into an enlarged rectum that absorbs excess water from any undigested food, and relatively dry excrement passes out the anus.*

c. The excretory system is made up of numerous tiny tubules, the **Malpighian tubules,** which empty their products into the anterior end of the intestine. These tubules remove wastes and salts from the blood. Locate these tubules.

d. Push aside the digestive tract and locate the **ventral nerve cord** lying medially inside the ventral body wall. Ganglia are expanded regions of the ventral nerve cord found in each body segment. Following the nerve cord anteriorly, note that branches from the nerve cord pass around the digestive tract and meet, forming a brain in the head.

Results

Complete Table 1, recording all information for grasshopper characteristics in the appropriate row. Use this information to complete Table 2 and answer questions in the Applying Your Knowledge section at the end of this lab topic.

Discussion

1. Describe how each of the following external structures helps the grasshopper live successfully in terrestrial environments.

   a. Exoskeleton

   b. Wings

   c. Large, jointed legs

   d. Spiracles

2. Describe how each of the following internal structures helps the grasshopper live successfully in terrestrial environments.

   a. Tracheae

   b. Malpighian tubules

   c. Rectum

EXERCISE 3
Deuterostome—Phylum
Echinodermata—Sea Star

Echinodermata is one of three phyla in the group of animals called deuterostomes. You will study another deuterostome phylum in Exercise 4, phylum Chordata. Examples of echinoderms include the sea star, sea urchin, sea cucumber, and sea lily. Some of the most familiar animals in the animal kingdom are in the phylum Chordata—fish, reptiles, amphibians, and mammals. Take a look at a sea star (starfish) in the salt-water aquarium in your lab or in a tidal pool on a rocky shore. What are the most obvious characteristics of this animal? Then imagine a chordate—a fish, dog, or even yourself. You might question why these two phyla are considered closely related phylogenetically. The most obvious difference is a very basic characteristic—the sea star has radial symmetry and most chordates that you imagine have bilateral symmetry. The sea star has no head or other obvious chordate features and it crawls around using hundreds of small suction cups called tube feet. Most chordates show strong cephalization and move using appendages. Your conclusion from the superficial observations might be that these two phyla are not closely related. Your observations are a good example of the difficulty faced by taxonomists when comparing animals based only on the morphology of adults. Taxonomists must collect data from studies of developmental and—as we discovered with the protostomes—molecular similarities before coming to final conclusions.

In this and the following exercise, you will examine an echinoderm, the adult sea star (demonstration only), and two chordates, asking questions about their morphology and adaptation to their habitats. You may not be convinced of their phylogentic relationships, however, until you study early development in sea urchins and sea stars. At that time, you will see that chordates and echinoderms have similar early embryonic developmental patterns, including the formation of the mouth and anus and the type of cleavage.

Materials

whole preserved sea stars on demonstration
several dissected sea stars on demonstration showing the internal contents of the body and the inside surface of oral and aboral halves of the body

Introduction

The sea star is classified in the phylum Echinodermata. They are marine animals with an endoskeleton of small, spiny calcareous plates bound together by connective tissue. Their symmetry is radial pentamerous (five-parted). They have no head or brain and few sensory structures. All animals in this phylum have a unique **water-vascular system** that develops from mesoderm and consists of a series of canals carrying water that enters the body through an outer opening, the **madreporite.** The canals are located inside the body and include a ring around the central disk of the body and tubes or canals that extend out into each arm. The canals then terminate in many small structures called **tube feet** along the groove on the

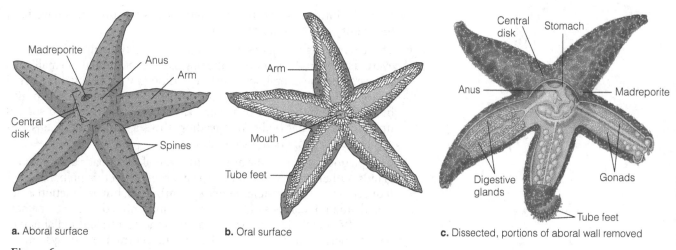

a. Aboral surface   **b.** Oral surface   **c.** Dissected, portions of aboral wall removed

Figure 6.
(a) Aboral surface of a sea star. (b) Oral surface of a sea star. (c) Dissected sea star with portions of the aboral wall removed.

oral side of each arm. Tube feet extend to the outside of the body and end in a small suction cup in most species. By contracting muscles and forcing fluid into its tube feet, the sea star can extend and attach the feet to hard surfaces such as the surface of a clamshell, or rocks on the ocean shore.

Procedure

1. Observe the preserved sea star on demonstration. Locate the **aboral** surface—the "upper" surface away from the mouth (Figure 6a). The downside is the **oral** surface where the mouth is located (Figure 6b).

2. Count the number of arms that extend out from the **central disk.** Echinoderms are usually pentamerous, meaning that their arms are in multiples of five. Occasionally a sea star with six arms will be found. Arms that are damaged or lost can be regenerated, and an extra arm may regenerate.

3. Observe the animal's aboral surface (Figure 6a). Locate the **madreporite,** a small porous plate displaced to one side of the central disk that serves to take water into the water vascular system.

   Notice that the surface of the animal's body is spiny. The spines project from calcareous plates of the **endoskeleton.** The endoskeleton is derived from the embryonic germ layer mesoderm. In life, the entire surface of the body is covered with an **epidermis** derived from ectoderm that may not be visible with the naked eye.

4. Observe the dissected sea star on demonstration (Figure 6c). In this dissection the entire aboral surface has been lifted off the body and placed to the side, inside up. This exposes the internal organs. The endoskeleton and its calcareous plates are obvious as viewed from the inside of the body.

5. Inside the body the organs are located in a **true body cavity.** Small delicate projections of the body cavity protrude between the plates of the endoskeleton to the outside of the body. These projections, covered with epidermis, are called **skin gills** or dermal branchiae, and function in the exchange of oxygen and carbon dioxide with the water bathing the animal's body. In addition, nitrogenous waste passes through these

skin gills into the surrounding water; these structures thus have both respiratory and excretory functions.

6. The central disk contains the stomach, a portion of which can be everted through the mouth on the oral side of the animal. A small anus is located on the aboral body surface, although very little fecal material is ejected here. Most digestion takes place in the stomach, which may be everted into the body of a clam. The digested broth is then sucked up into the sea star body. After feeding, the sea star draws in its stomach by contracting its stomach muscles.

7. Conspicuous organs in the arms of the animal are gonads and digestive glands. Other systems cannot be easily observed in this preparation. A reduced circulatory system (hemal system) exists, but its function is not well defined. It consists of tissue strands and unlined sinuses. The nervous system includes a nerve ring around the mouth and radial nerves with epidermal nerve networks.There is no central nervous system.

Results

Complete Table 1, recording in the appropriate row all information you have been able to observe. Use this information to complete Table 2 and answer questions in the Applying Your Knowledge section at the end of this lab topic.

Student Media Video—Ch. 33: Echinoderm Tube Feet

Discussion

1. Imagine that you are a zoologist studying sea stars for the first time. What characteristics would you note from the dissection of an adult animal that might give a clue to its phylogenetic relationships—that it belongs with deuterostomes rather than protostomes?

2. What structures have you observed that appear to be unique to echinoderms?

3. How would you continue your study to obtain more information that might help in classifying these animals?

4. Given the fact that other deuterostomes are bilaterally symmetrical, what is one explanation for the radial symmetry of most adult echinoderms?

EXERCISE 4
Deuterostome—Phylum Chordata

Up to this point, all the animals you have studied are commonly called **invertebrates,** a somewhat artificial designation based on the absence of a backbone. Those animals with a backbone are called **vertebrates.** The phylum Chordata studied in this exercise includes two subphyla of invertebrates and a third subphylum of vertebrates, animals that have a bony or cartilaginous endoskeleton with a vertebral column. Chordates inhabit terrestrial and aquatic (freshwater and marine) environments. One group has developed the ability to fly. The body plan of chordates is unique in that these animals demonstrate a complex of four important characteristics at some stage in their development. In this exercise, you will discover these characteristics.

You will study two chordate species: the lancelet, an invertebrate in the subphylum Cephalochordata, and the pig, a vertebrate in the subphylum Vertebrata. The third subphylum, Urochordata, will not be studied.

Lab Study A. Lancelets (*Branchiostoma,* formerly *Amphioxus*)

Materials

compound microscope
stereoscopic microscope
preserved lancelet in watch glass

prepared slide of whole mount of
    lancelet
prepared slide of cross section of
    lancelet

Introduction

Lancelets are marine animals that burrow in sand in tidal flats. They feed with their head end extended from their burrow. They resemble fish superficially, but their head is poorly developed, and they have unique features not found in fish or other vertebrates. They retain the four unique characteristics of chordates throughout their life cycle and are excellent animals to use to demonstrate these features. In this lab study, you will observe preserved lancelets, prepared slides of whole mounts, and cross sections through the body of a lancelet.

Procedure

1. Place a preserved lancelet in water in a watch glass and observe it using the stereoscopic microscope. Handle the specimen with care and *do not dissect it*. Note the fishlike shape of the slender, elongate body. Locate the anterior end by the presence at that end of a noselike **rostrum** extending over the mouth region, surrounded by small tentacles. Notice the lack of a well-defined head. Look for the segmented muscles that surround much of the animal's body. Can you see signs of a tail? If the animal you are studying is mature, you will be able to see two rows of 20 to 25 white gonads on the ventral surface of the body.

2. Return the specimen to the correct container.

3. Observe the whole mount slide of the lancelet and compare your observations with Figure 7.

 Use only the lowest power on the compound microscope to study this slide.

a. Scan the entire length of the body wall. Do you see evidence of segmentation in the muscles?

b. Look at the anterior end of the animal. Do you see evidence of a sensory system? Describe what you see.

Figure 7.
The lancelet, whole mount. The rostrum extends over the mouth region. The pharynx, including the pharyngeal gill slits, leads to the intestine, which exits the body at the anus. Note that a tail extends beyond the anus. Structures positioned from the dorsal surface of the body inward include a dorsal fin, the nerve cord, and the notochord.

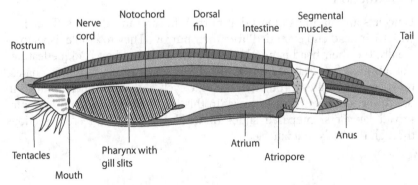

Adapted from L. Mitchell, J. Mutchmor, and W. Dolphin, *Zoology* (Menlo Park, CA: Benjamin/Cummings, 1988), © 1988 The Benjamin/Cummings Publishing Company.

c. Locate the mouth of the animal at the anterior end. See if you can follow a tube from just under the rostrum into a large sac with numerous gill slits. This sac is the **pharynx with gill slits,** a uniquely chordate structure. Water and food pass into the pharynx from the mouth. Food passes posteriorly from the pharynx into the intestine, which ends at the anus on the ventral side of the animal, several millimeters before the end. The extension of the body beyond the anus is called a **post-anal tail.** You may have studied worms in a previous lab. If so, where was the anus located in these animals? Was a post-anal region present? Explain.

d. Water entering the mouth passes through the gill slits and collects in a chamber, the **atrium,** just inside the body wall. The water ultimately passes out of the body at a ventral pore, the **atripore.** Surprisingly, the gill slits are not the major gas exchange surface in the lancelet body. Because of the great activity of ciliated cells in this region, it is even possible that blood leaving the gill region has less oxygen than that entering the region. The function of gill slits is simply to strain food from the water. The major site for gas exchange is the body surface.

e. Now turn your attention to the dorsal side of the animal. Beginning at the surface of the body and moving inward, identify the listed structures and speculate about the function of each one.

dorsal fin:

nerve cord:

notochord:

The nerve cord is in a dorsal position. Have you seen only a dorsal nerve cord in any of the animals previously studied?

The notochord is a cartilage-like rod that lies ventral to the nerve cord and extends the length of the body. Have you seen a notochord in any of the previous animals?

The lancelet circulatory system is not visible in these preparations, but the animal has **closed circulation** with dorsal and ventral aortae, capillaries, and veins. Excretory organs, or nephridia (not visible here), are located near the true coelom, which surrounds the pharynx.

4. Observe the slide of cross sections taken through the lancelet body. There may be several sections on this slide, taken at several positions along the length of the body. Find the section through the pharynx and compare it with Figure 8.

✳ Study this slide on the lowest power.

In cross section, it is much easier to see the structural relationships among the various organs of the lancelet. Identify the following structures and label them on Figure 8.

a. **Segmental muscles.** They are located on each side of the body, under the skin.

b. **Dorsal fin.** This projects upward from the most dorsal surface of the body.

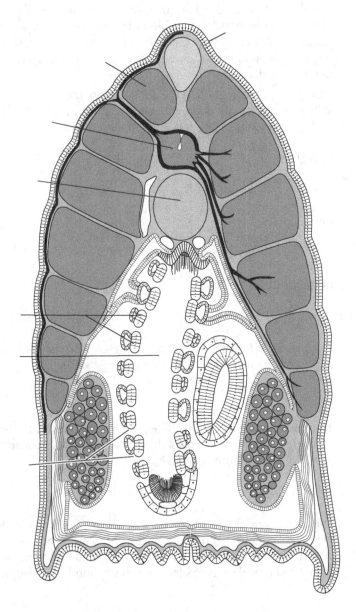

Figure 8.
Cross section through the
pharyngeal region of the lancelet.

   c. **Nerve cord.** You may be able to see that the nerve cord contains a small central canal, thus making it hollow. The nerve cord is located in the dorsal region of the body, ventral to the dorsal fin between the lateral bundles of muscle.

   d. **Notochord.** This is a large oval structure located just ventral to the nerve cord.

   e. **Pharynx with gill slits.** This structure appears as a series of dark triangles arranged in an oval. The triangles are cross sections of **gill bars.** The spaces between the triangles are **gill slits,** through which water passes into the surrounding chamber.

Results

1. Complete the diagram of the lancelet cross section in Figure 8. Label all the structures listed in step 4 of the Procedure section.

2. Complete Table 1, recording all information for lancelet characteristics in the appropriate row. Use this information to complete Table 2 and answer questions in the Applying Your Knowledge section at the end of this lab topic.

Discussion

Describe the uniquely chordate features that you have detected in the lancelet that were not present in the animals previously studied.

Lab Study B. Fetal Pigs (*Sus scrofa*)

Materials

preserved fetal pig   disposable gloves
dissecting pan

Introduction

The pig is a terrestrial vertebrate. In this lab study, working with your lab partner, you will observe external features only, observing those characteristics studied in other animals in previous exercises. Compare the organization of the vertebrate body with the animals previously studied. As you dissect the pig in subsequent labs, come back to these questions and answer the ones that cannot be answered in today's lab study.

Procedure

1. Obtain a preserved fetal pig from the class supply and carry it to your desk in a dissecting pan.

 Use disposable gloves to handle preserved animals.

2. With your lab partner, read each of the following questions. Drawing on observations you have made of other animals in the animal diversity lab studies, predict the answer to each question about the fetal pig. Then examine the fetal pig and determine the answer, if possible. Give evidence for your answer based on your observations of the pig, your knowledge of vertebrate anatomy, or your understanding of animal phylogeny.

a. What type of symmetry does the pig body have?

Prediction:

Evidence:

b. How many layers of embryonic tissue are present?
Prediction:

Evidence:

c. Are cells organized into distinct tissues?
Prediction:

Evidence:

d. How many digestive tract openings are present? Would you describe this as a "tube within a tube"?
Prediction:

Evidence:

e. Is the circulatory system open or closed?
Prediction:

Evidence:

f. What is the habitat of the animal?
    Prediction:

    Evidence:

g. What are the organs for respiration?
    Prediction:

    Evidence:

h. What are the organs for excretion?
    Prediction:

    Evidence:

i. What is the method of locomotion?
    Prediction:

    Evidence:

j. Are support systems internal or external?
    Prediction:

    Evidence:

k. Is the body segmented?
    Prediction:

    Evidence:

l. Are appendages present?
Prediction:

Evidence:

m. What is the position and complexity of the nervous system?
Prediction:

Evidence:

Results

Complete Table 1, recording all information for pig characteristics in the appropriate row. Use this information to complete Table 2 and answer questions in the Applying Your Knowledge section that follows.

Questions for Review

1. Complete the summary table, Table 1, recording in the appropriate row information about characteristics of all animals studied.
2. Using Table 1, complete Table 2. Categorize all animals studied based on the 13 basic characteristics. Use this information to answer questions in the Applying Your Knowledge section that follows.

Applying Your Knowledge

1. Using specific examples from the animals you have studied, describe ways that organisms have adapted to specific environments.
   a. Compare organisms adapted to aquatic environments with those from terrestrial environments.
   b. Compare adaptations of the parasitic *Ascaris* with the earthworm or clamworm, free-living organisms.

2. The phylum Platyhelminthes also includes many examples of parasitic flatworms, for example, tapeworms and trematodes (flukes). Using Web resources, choose an example of a parasitic flatworm and compare morphological differences between this organism and the planarian that reflect specific life-style adaptations.

3. In your studies of animal phyla, you observed segmentation in widely diverse clades, for example, annelids (Lophotrochozoa), arthropods (Ecdysozoa), and chordates (Deuterostomia). How can you explain this in terms of their evolutionary history?

4. Upon superficial examination, the body form of certain present-day animals might be described as simple, yet these animals may have developed specialized structures, perhaps unique to their particular phylum. Illustrate this point using examples from some of the simpler organisms you have dissected.

5. One might conclude that certain trends can be detected, trends from ancestral features (those that arose early in the evolution of animals) to more derived traits (those that arose later). However, animals with ancestral characteristics still successfully exist on Earth today. Why is this so? Why have the animals with derived traits not completely replaced the ones with ancestral traits? Use examples from the lab to illustrate your answer.

6. A major theme in biology is the relationship between form and function in organisms. Select one of the major characteristics from Table 1, and illustrate the relationship of form and function for this characteristic using examples from the organisms studied.

Table 1
Summary Table of Animal Characteristics

Animal	Symmetry	Tissue Organization	Type of Body Cavity	Digestive Openings	Circulatory System	Habitat	Respiratory Organs
Sponge							
Hydra							
Planarian							
Clamworm/ earthworm							
Clam							
Roundworm							
Crayfish							
Grasshopper							
Sea star							
Lancelet							
Pig							

Table 1

Summary Table of Animal Characterstics (*continued*)

Animal	Excretory System	Locomotion	Support System	Segmentation	Appendages	Nervous System Organization
Sponge						
Hydra						
Planarian						
Clamworm/ earthworm						
Clam						
Roundworm						
Crayfish						
Grasshopper						
Sea star						
Lancelet						
Pig						

Table 2
Comparison of Organisms by Major Features

1. Tissue Organization	5. Circulatory System
a. distinct tissues absent:	a. none:
b. distinct tissues present:	b. open:
2. Symmetry	c. closed:
a. radial:	**6. Habitat**
b. bilateral:	a. aquatic:
3. Body Cavity	b. terrestrial:
a. acoelomate:	c. parasitic:
b. pseudocoelomate:	
c. eucoelomate:	**7. Organs for Gas Exchange**
	a. skin:
4. Openings to Digestive Tract	b. gills:
a. one:	c. lungs:
b. two:	d. spiracles/tracheae:

Table 2
Comparison of Organisms by Major Features (*continued*)

8. Organs for Excretion (list organ and animals)	**11. Segmented Body** a. no: b. yes:
	12. Appendages a. yes: b. no:
9. Type of Locomotion (list type and animals)	**13. Nervous System** a. ventral nerve cord:
10. Support System a. external: b. internal: c. hydrostatic:	b. dorsal nerve cord: c. other:

Student Media Activities and Investigations

Activities—Ch. 32: Animal Phylogenetic Tree; Ch. 33: Characteristics of Invertebrates; Ch. 34: Characteristics of Chordates

Investigations—Ch. 32: How Do molecular Data Fit Traditional Phylogenies? Ch. 33: How Are Insect Species Identified?

www.masteringbio.com

Investigative Extensions

1. Scientists worldwide are concerned about reports of global warming. Crayfish are common inhabitants of freshwater streams, ponds, and swamps, all of which may be affected by a warming earth. Design an experiment to test the thermal limits that can be tolerated by crayfish.

   Design similar experiments to test the effects of pesticides, fertilizers, herbicides, petroleum products, or human wastes—all of which may be present in runoff into crayfish habitat from farmlands or urban development.

2. Arthropods are the dominant animals on the earth, both in number of species and number of individuals. Now that you are familiar with the characteristics of insects (terrestrial arthropods), using an entomology (study of insects) text or insect identification key, determine the diversity of arthropods, or specifically insects, found in various habitats. You might sample a given amount of soil taken from several different environments. For example, you might compare arthropod diversity in a deciduous forest with that of a cultivated field with that of a manicured lawn.

   You might also investigate arthropod diversity in habitats that differ in moisture. Compare well-drained soil (along a ridge) with saturated soil (along a creek, in a marsh, or in a bog).

3. N. A. Cobb, famous nematologist, writes: "If all the matter in the universe except the nematodes were swept away, our world would still be dimly recognizable . . . We should find its mountains, hills, vales, rivers, lakes, and oceans represented by a film of nematodes" (1915). Nematodes are everywhere and many are readily available for study.

   Design an experiment to investigate the diversity of nematodes present in several sources; for example, fresh and rotting fruits, soils collected from different sources or treated with different chemicals, roots of plants—trees or vegetables grown for human consumption. (Many nematodes are plant parasites, and many have been imported on foods or nursery stock.)

   Are there nematodes in drinking water? How could you investigate this question? How could you collect the nematodes?

References

Aguinaldo, A. M., J. M. Turbeville, L. S. Linford, M. C. Rivera, J. R. Garey, R. A. Raff, J. A. Lake. "Evidence for a Clade of Nematodes, Arthropods, and other Moulting Animals." *Nature*, 29 May 1997 (387), pp. 489–493.

Cobb, N. A. "Nematodes and Their Relationships." Year Book Dept. Agric. 1914, pp. 457–490. Washington, DC: Dept. Agric. 1915.

Hickman, C. P., L. S. Roberts, A. Larson, and H. I'Anson. *Integrated Principles of Zoology*, 12th ed. Boston: McGraw Hill, 2004.

Websites

Includes descriptions of many invertebrates and vertebrates, links to insect keys, references:
http://animaldiversity.ummz.umich.edu/index.html

The Tree of Life web project provides information on all major groups of organisms, including invertebrates:
http://tolweb.org/Bilateria

Report of an experiment testing nematodes for space experiments:
http://news-service.stanford.edu/News/2004/february/worms-24.html.

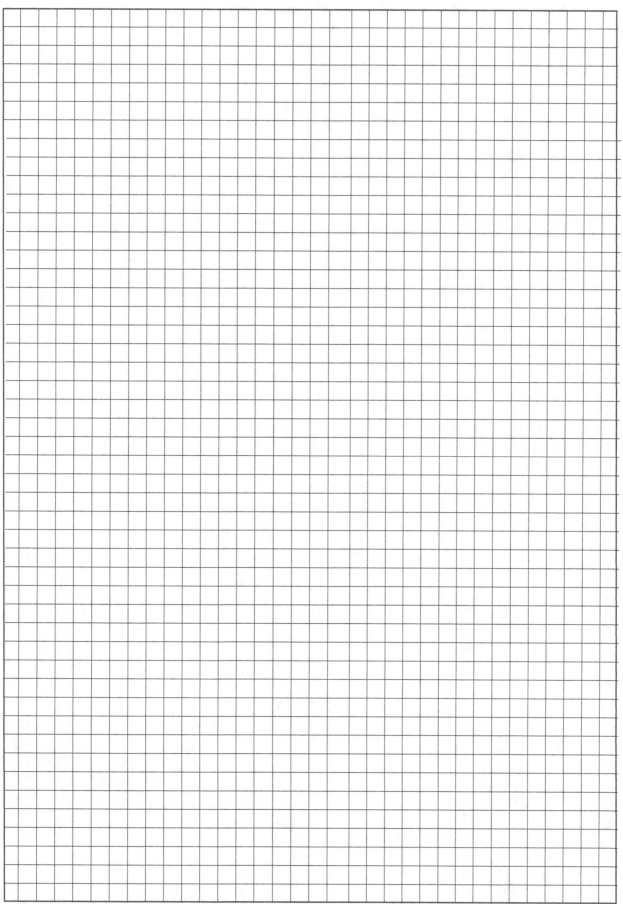

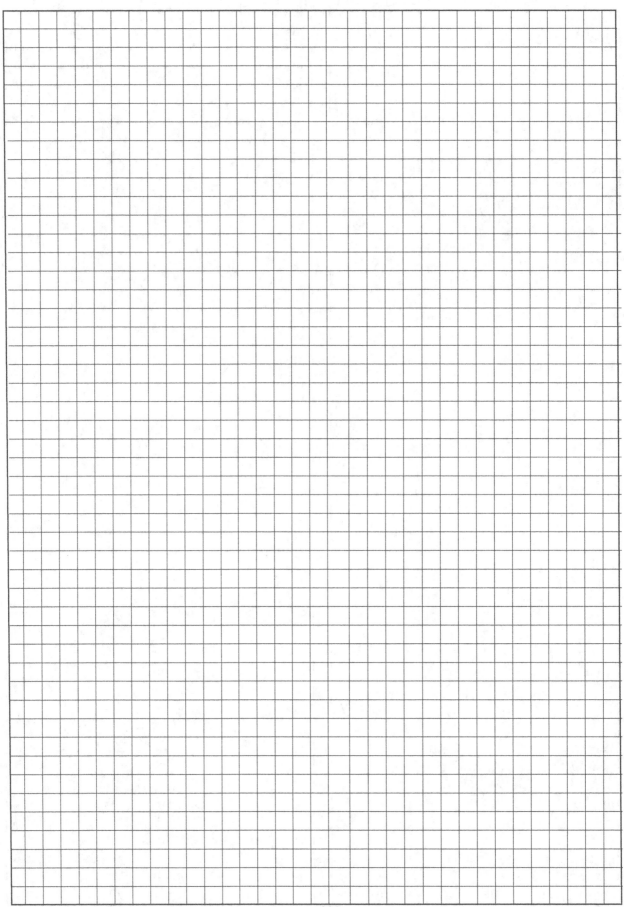

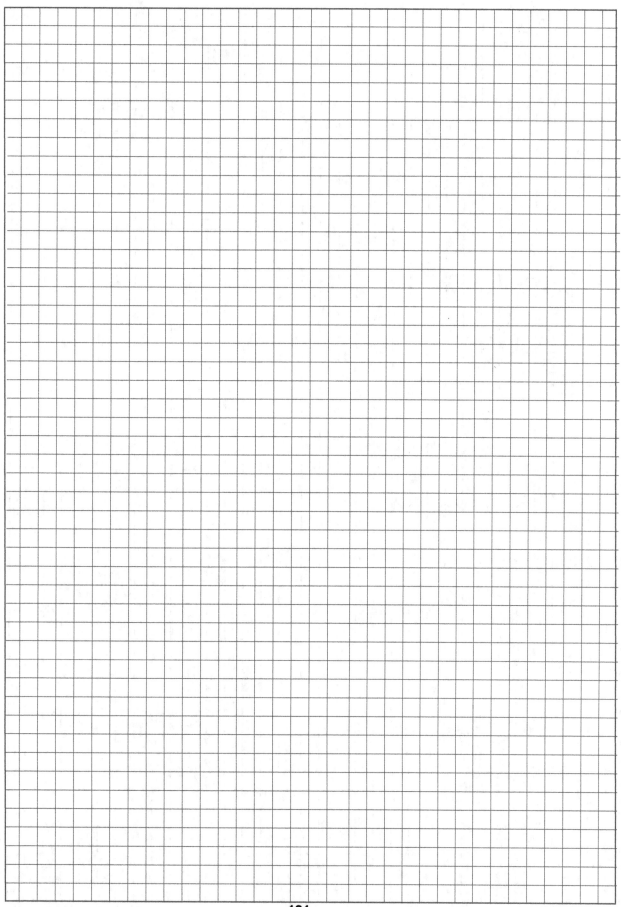

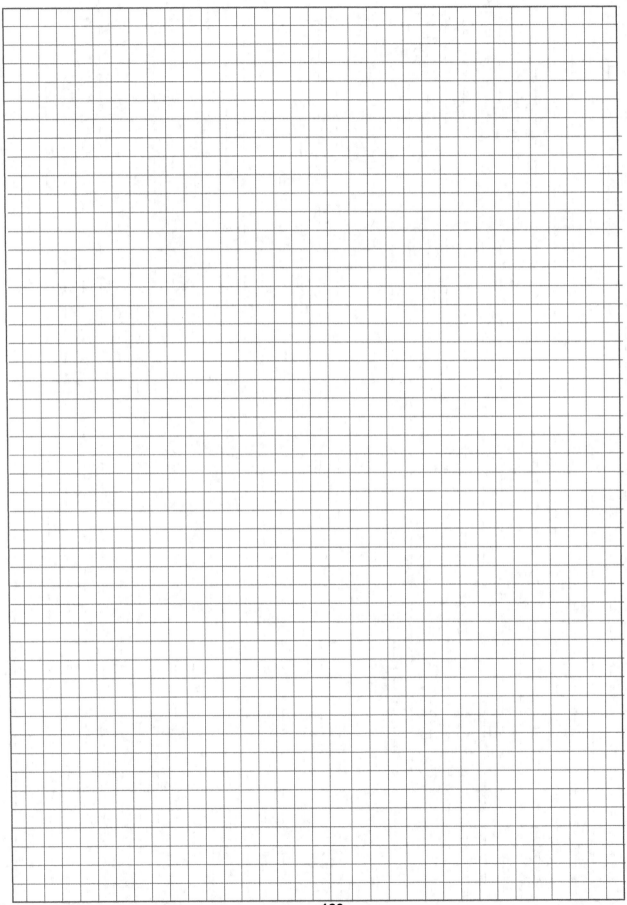

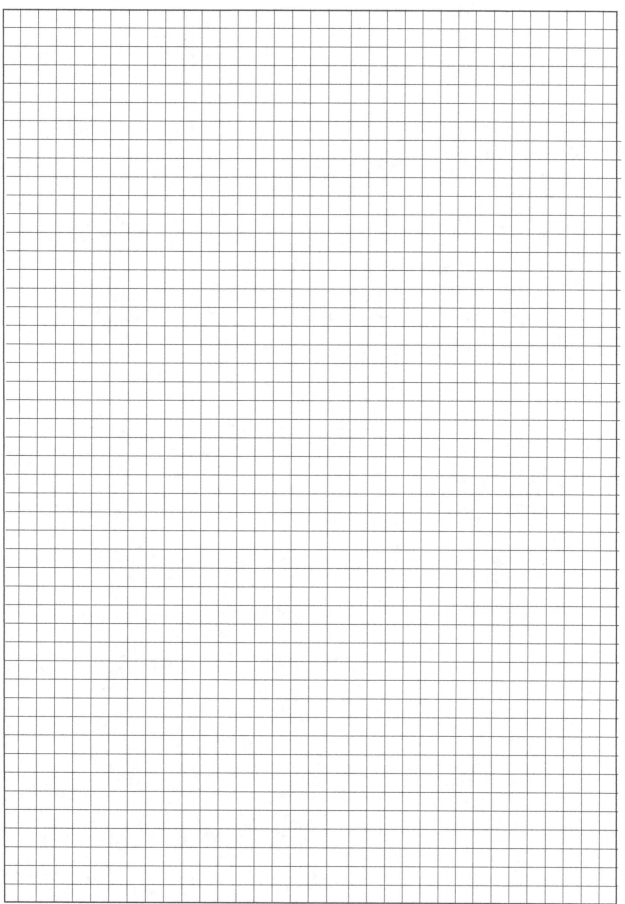